D1096609

VoIP: Internet Linking for Radio Amateurs

Jonathan Taylor, K1RFD

Published by
ARRL—the national association for Amateur Radio
Newington, CT 06111 USA

CONTENTS

FOREWORD

When the Internet burst onto the public stage in the early 1990s, some amateurs were fearful. They worried that the Internet would somehow replace the avocation that they had grown to love.

In the years that followed, however, it quickly became clear that the Internet was *complementing* Amateur Radio, not replacing it. Hams put the Internet to work as a medium for rapid exchange of information and ideas. Advances in digital amateur communication and software-defined radio had their genesis in exchanges that took place on the Internet.

Amateurs also realized that the Internet could serve as a communications "pipeline" to link distant locations in a reliable manner that isn't always possible with satellites or HF communication. Thanks to amateur ingenuity, we now have new communication systems that unite radio with the Internet in ways never imagined just a few years ago.

One system uses Voice Over Internet Protocol, or *VoIP*, to exchange voice communication using the Internet to bridge individual radio stations. By using VoIP networks, hams who were once limited to local communication because of antenna restrictions and other issues can now talk to the world.

VoIP: Internet Linking for Radio Amateurs is your guide to VoIP. The author is Jonathan Taylor, K1RFD, the creator of *EchoLink*, one of the most popular amateur VoIP networks. But Jonathan doesn't confine this book to a discussion of *EchoLink*. On the contrary, *VoIP: Internet Linking for Radio Amateurs* explores other systems in detail, including the Internet Radio Linking Project, (*IRLP*), *eQSO* and *WIRES*.

VoIP: Internet Linking for Radio Amateurs is written in way that any amateur can understand, regardless of technical ability. In this book, you find a wealth of helpful information to make your VoIP experience as enjoyable as possible.

Please take a few minutes to give us your comments and suggestions on this book. There's a handy Feedback Form for this purpose at the back, or you can send e-mail to: **pubsfdbk@arrl.org**.

David Sumner, K1ZZ
Executive Vice President
Newington, Connecticut
May 2009

ABOUT THE ARRL

The seed for Amateur Radio was planted in the 1890s, when Guglielmo Marconi began his experiments in wireless telegraphy. Soon he was joined by dozens, then hundreds, of others who were enthusiastic about sending and receiving messages through the air—some with a commercial interest, but others solely out of a love for this new communications medium. The United States government began licensing Amateur Radio operators in 1912.

By 1914, there were thousands of Amateur Radio operators—hams—in the United States. Hiram Percy Maxim, a leading Hartford, Connecticut inventor and industrialist, saw the need for an organization to band together this fledgling group of radio experimenters. In May 1914 he founded the American Radio Relay League (ARRL) to meet that need.

Today ARRL, with approximately 150,000 members, is the largest organization of radio amateurs in the United States. The ARRL is a not-for-profit organization that:
- promotes interest in Amateur Radio communications and experimentation
- represents US radio amateurs in legislative matters, and
- maintains fraternalism and a high standard of conduct among Amateur Radio operators.

At ARRL headquarters in the Hartford suburb of Newington, the staff helps serve the needs of members. ARRL is also International Secretariat for the International Amateur Radio Union, which is made up of similar societies in 150 countries around the world.

ARRL publishes the monthly journal *QST*, as well as newsletters and many publications covering all aspects of Amateur Radio. Its headquarters station, W1AW, transmits bulletins of interest to radio amateurs and Morse code practice sessions. The ARRL also coordinates an extensive field organization, which includes volunteers who provide technical information and other support services for radio amateurs as well as communications for public-service activities. In addition, ARRL represents US amateurs with the Federal Communications Commission and other government agencies in the US and abroad.

Membership in ARRL means much more than receiving *QST* each month. In addition to the services already described, ARRL offers membership services on a personal level, such as the Technical Information Service—where members can get answers by phone, email or the ARRL website, to all their technical and operating questions.

Full ARRL membership (available only to licensed radio amateurs) gives you a voice in how the affairs of the organization are governed. ARRL policy is set by a Board of Directors (one from each of 15 Divisions). Each year, one-third of the ARRL Board of Directors stands for election by the full members they represent. The day-to-day operation of ARRL HQ is managed by an Executive Vice President and his staff.

No matter what aspect of Amateur Radio attracts you, ARRL membership is relevant and important. There would be no Amateur Radio as we know it today were it not for the ARRL.

We would be happy to welcome you as a member! (An Amateur Radio license is not required for Associate Membership.) For more information about ARRL and answers to any questions you may have about Amateur Radio, write or call:

ARRL—The national association for Amateur Radio
225 Main Street
Newington CT 06111-1494
Voice: 860-594-0200
Fax: 860-594-0259
E-mail: **hq@arrl.org**
Internet: **www.arrl.org/**

Prospective new amateurs call (toll-free):
800-32-NEW HAM (800-326-3942)
You can also contact us via e-mail at **newham@arrl.org**
or check out *ARRLWeb* at **www.arrl.org/**

ABOUT THIS BOOK

This book introduces Internet linking, and describes several of the most widely-used systems, with particular attention to *EchoLink* and the Internet Radio Linking Project, or *IRLP*. It gives some basic advice about how to operate an Internet link, how to plan, set up and customize your own. It also provides a peek into the innards of these systems, with some background on how Voice over Internet Protocol, or VoIP, works, and some of the digital magic that goes on behind the scenes.

Internet linking is a relatively new and fast-moving aspect of Amateur Radio, and I won't try to dive deeply into the details of how to set up and configure each individual system. At this level, each system is quite different, and software can change substantially with each new release. Fortunately, plenty of useful documentation is available online. See the "Resources" chapter at the end of the book for helpful links.

Chapter 1

Connecting the World

Hurricane Isabel slams into the coast of North Carolina, unleashing 95-knot winds and a six-foot storm surge, knocking out electric power and local telephone communications. Despite unfavorable HF propagation, local weather reports are relayed by Amateur Radio operators, using handheld radios, directly to the National Hurricane Center in Florida. Damage reports and health-and-welfare information is routed directly to emergency operations centers and Red Cross centers hundreds of miles away. Amateur Radio steps in when many other communications systems fail.

The space shuttle Columbia disintegrates over eastern Texas, scattering debris over a broad swath. Radio Amateurs spring into action, locating debris and exchanging precise location reports with hams in nearby counties, who are assisting local law enforcement and NASA. Questions about Columbia's demise are quickly getting answers.

A retired electrical engineer who had been an active member of his local radio club in the Northeast begins a new life in Florida, and faces the prospect of remaining out of touch with old friends because of strict outdoor antenna restrictions. But he still manages to check into his club's daily 2-meter net back home, just as if he'd never left. Friendships strengthened by Amateur Radio remain strong as ever.

All of this is made possible by an intriguing marriage of perhaps the two greatest communications inventions of the twentieth century: Radio and the Internet. Hams in the twenty-first century now find themselves in the perfect position to join these two technologies together. Through a technique called *Internet linking*, they are harnessing the immediacy and portability of radio communication to the global reach of the Internet, and all sorts of new possibilities are emerging.

STRANGE BEDFELLOWS?

Amateur Radio has more in common with the Internet than you might realize. Today's Internet began as the vision of DARPA, the U.S. Government's Defense Advanced Research Projects Agency. The idea was to create a coast-to-coast digital network which could route messages from anywhere to anywhere, with plenty of extra paths in place so that the whole thing would hold together even after a nuclear weapons strike, or a devastating natural disaster. Even back in the 1970s, the system worked well. Colleges and universities began hooking up their computers to ARPANET, finding it a cost-effective way to exchange research information. Large corporations began using the network — which now spanned the globe, and had become known as the Internet — to exchange e-mail. Then, in the early 1990s, the invention of the graphical Web browser ignited an explosion of Internet usage. Millions and millions of computers are now interconnected, many of which are PCs in homes.

Amateur Radio, although it hasn't seen the same growth spurt (imagine the QRM!), is also global, immediate, and fault-tolerant. We already know that hams are sometimes the only link to the outside world from the site of a disaster, with mobile and portable stations often proving most valuable to relay traffic directly from the scene.

So why not experiment with connecting the two together?

Some enterprising hams had exactly this thought in the mid-1990s, when the Internet began coming into homes in earnest, and thus also into ham shacks. The idea was this: Using personal computers equipped with sound cards, connect the audio signals of two FM rigs to each other over the Internet. This allows mobile and portable stations in the coverage area of one station to establish voice communication with stations in the coverage area of the other, without limitations imposed by distance, terrain, or HF propagation (**Figure 1.1**).

Sending data (including voice signals) over the Internet is certainly nothing new. What makes this idea interesting is that Amateur Radio stations can harness this technology to produce a hybrid system that is part RF and part Internet, taking advantage of the inherent strengths of both techniques.

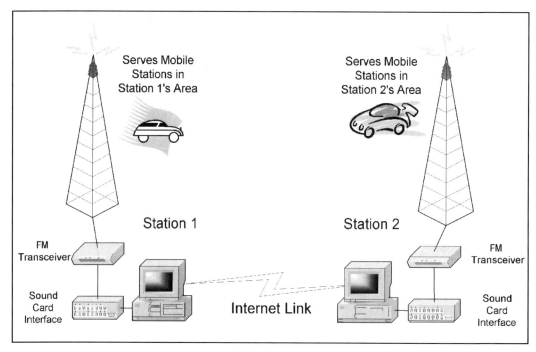

Figure 1.1 — By interconnecting two FM simplex stations over the Internet, the coverage areas of the two stations are effectively combined.

EARLY EXPERIMENTS

In the mid-1990s, a program called *Internet Phone* began to make the rounds. It was one of the first voice-over-IP (VoIP) programs widely available to the public. The idea was that you could use the microphone and speaker connected to your Internet-attached PC to make telephone calls to any similarly equipped computer anywhere in the world, for free! As long as you knew the Internet address of the computer you wanted to hook up with, you could simply type it in, establish a connection, and start talking. Sure, there were occasional "drop outs" (gaps in the audio) due to the slow modems at each end, but the experience of hearing someone else's voice coming from the computer speakers was stunning.

Naturally, once a few enterprising hams began experimenting with *Internet Phone*, they got the idea that it could easily be adapted to join VHF-FM stations together. Rather than connecting a microphone and speakers to the computer's sound card, why not connect the sound card to the microphone and speaker jacks of an FM transceiver? This would allow anyone within range of the transceiver connected to Computer A to communicate with anyone within range of the rig connected to Computer B. Sure enough, it worked (sort of), and one of the first Internet voice links between two Amateur stations was established.

The next logical step was to tune the "linked" transceiver to the frequency pair of a local repeater, rather than a simplex frequency. This opened up even more possibilities, since now any station in range of the repeater at either end could be part of the long-distance QSO. Things were starting to get interesting!

In 1996, Mark Brown, N9YNQ, developed a *Windows* program called *Repeater Link*. *Repeater Link* formed a software bridge between *Internet Phone* and an FM rig connected to the PC through a special hardware interface concocted by Jack Leverich, KC9KY. The *Repeater Link* system may have been the first PC-based Amateur Radio VoIP linking system. (Perhaps Mark and Jack can lay claim to being the Alexander Graham Bell and Thomas Watson of Internet linking.)

Unfortunately, like many early Internet experiments, technology took a while to catch up. There was plenty of talk about broadband Internet access in the mid-90s, and not very much action. (Remember ISDN service from the telephone company? The running joke was that ISDN actually stood for "It Still Does Nothing.") Without reliable, dedicated Internet access coming into the ham shack or the repeater site, widespread Internet linking would have to wait.

Fortunately, broadband did finally arrive, and so did fast, cheap personal computers. Today, millions of Americans have Internet access in their homes delivered by TV cable, digital subscriber line (DSL), or satellite. Dial-up modems have improved, too, as have the quality of (some) phone lines. Coming from the opposite direction, audio and video compression technologies have improved, and personal computers are more efficient than ever before at processing this information, and quite a bit cheaper, cycle for cycle. See the sidebar, **"Moore's Law."**

LET THE LINKING BEGIN!

Fueled partly by the improvements in Internet bandwidth, more voice-over-IP Internet linking systems began to spring up. One of the most successful was (and still is) the Internet Radio Linking Project, or *IRLP*. *IRLP* begin experimenting in the fall of 1997 with using the Internet to link several Amateur systems in Canada, with the first full-time hookup running coast-to-coast between Vancouver and Saint John, New Brunswick. After a few false starts, Dave Cameron, VE7LTD, settled on the open-source operating system called *Linux* as the platform for the next generation of *IRLP*. Since then, *IRLP* has flourished into a reliable, worldwide network, with more than 1,400 repeaters and simplex stations by 2008.

A few other enterprising hams continued experimenting with *Windows*-based systems, on which the original *Internet Phone* experiments had been conducted. In 2001, Graeme Barnes, MØCSH, developed a program called *iLINK,* which had two compelling features: It allowed access directly from a desktop computer, and it worked remarkably well over conventional dial-up Internet connections. This helped put Internet linking in the hands of thousands of hams who already had *Windows*-based computers and dial-up Internet access, and gave rise to a whole new classification of Internet-linked Amateur "stations" — licensed Amateurs who were connecting themselves to distant repeaters using only a computer.

The doors opened even wider with *eQSO,* developed by Paul Davies, MØZPD. Like *iLINK, eQSO* runs on conventional *Windows* PCs, and allows direct PC-based access to remote links. It specifically permits access by non-hams, either in a listen-only mode, or in off-air conferences. *eQSO* remains popular today.

Yaesu (Vertex Standard) entered the world of Amateur Internet linking with a hardware-software product called *WIRES-II*, in 2002. In conjunction with a set of Internet-based servers operated by Yaesu, the product functions similarly to some of the other linking systems, providing a "plug-and-play" solution for hams wishing to set up a link on a *Windows*-based computer.

Following the success of *iLINK*, my own contribution (in mid-2002) was a compatible software package called *EchoLink*. The program was originally designed to offer an alternative look-and-feel and feature set for *iLINK* users, but quickly evolved into a complete system of its own, due to its rapid (and unexpected) rate of acceptance. By 2008, *EchoLink* had been installed and registered by more than 200,000 licensed hams in 147 countries, and typically carried more than 3,300 repeaters and simplex links and about 700 PC-based users at any given time. More than half of the active users are outside the United States.

Although Internet linking has been going full-tilt for a number of years, it's interesting to see that activity is still as strong as ever. It seems that Internet linking has finally come of age!

WHAT IS INTERNET LINKING?

Hams have come up with various ways of joining Amateur Radio to the Internet, but *Internet linking*, in the context of this book, refers to using the Internet to connect Amateur Radio stations to each other to exchange voice signals. Since Amateur Internet linking uses VoIP to accomplish this feat, Internet linking is sometimes simply called VoIP.

As you know, ham stations take on many different forms, and the ones most commonly used with Internet links are FM repeater stations and simplex stations on the VHF and UHF bands. Some systems extend the definition of a "station" to include "remote base" types of operation, where one end of the link is a licensed Amateur sitting in front of a computer rather than a radio.

VHF/UHF FM is a natural mode for Internet-linked stations, since it's geared toward low-power portable and mobile stations, which have the greatest need for widely extended coverage. And for any kind of automatic relay, including Internet links, FM works well because of its good voice quality and positive squelch action. Finally, Internet links are a natural extension to the function of existing FM repeaters, many of which already have sophisticated controllers that provide additional services beyond basic radio relay.

SOFTWARE, SERVICES, AND SYSTEMS

The most basic type of Internet link is shown in **Figure 1.2**. At each end of the connection, audio from the receiver is piped into the sound card of a PC, where it is converted to digital packets and transmitted over the Internet to the other end. Then, the data is converted back into sound and fed into the microphone jack of a transmitter. The whole process is reversible, so that the two stations can carry on a QSO.

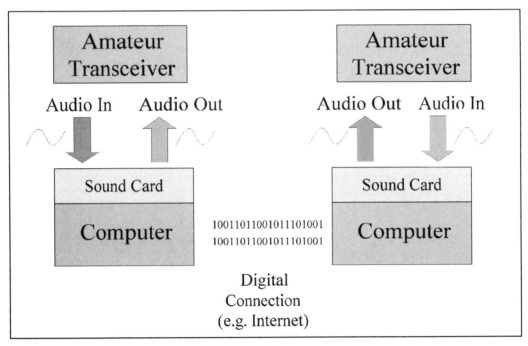

Figure 1.2 — Components of a basic point-to-point VoIP system.

This kind of setup might be fine for a permanent, point-to-point link, but the real power of Internet linking is its ability to make *ad hoc* connections to other stations, when and where needed. In order for this to work, at least three new ingredients must be thrown in:

1) Common software, or standard protocols. Each station in the system needs to be running software which is the same, or which is designed to interoperate with others, so that any station can connect to any other and be able to exchange signals.

2) Control. Besides simply exchanging voice signals, there should be some agreed-upon way to establish a new link, and to release it.

3) Directory services. The Internet uses numeric addresses rather than call signs, so there needs to be some way to locate a distant station on the Internet, such as by its call sign or node number.

4) Security. Since the Internet is a public network, each link needs some efficient way to restrict access, and to identify which station is connecting.

To satisfy these needs, *linking systems* have emerged. Each of these systems is a package that includes software (and sometimes hardware), plus services. Broadly speaking, the software takes care of requirements 1 and 2, and the services take care of requirements 3 and 4.

Chapter 2

Using a VoIP Link

If you're already comfortable with FM simplex and repeater operating procedures, using an Internet link will be an easy transition. For the most part, carrying on a QSO over an Internet link isn't much different from speaking with local stations on the repeater. But as with every Amateur mode, there are a few important guidelines to follow.

MAKING THE CONNECTION

A popular misconception about VoIP linking is that you need a computer to use it. Not at all! In most cases, you can fire up the link using the Dual Tone Multiple Frequency (DTMF) pad on your transceiver or handheld transceiver.

Most systems have a set of standard DTMF codes that can be used to connect to another station, or disconnect. As long as you're in range of the link (or the repeater to which it is linked), and operation by traveling users is welcomed, you can connect to any other Internet-linked station in the world from your transceiver. Before using a VoIP node, check with the node owner (or club) to see what the operating policies are.

With *EchoLink*, *IRLP*, and *WIRES-II*, every station on the system is assigned a unique *node number*. Node numbers are four, five, or six digits long. If you know the node number of the station you want to connect to, you can usually punch it in directly to initiate a contact. By default, on *EchoLink* and *IRLP*, no special prefix or suffix is required. However, each node owner has the option of customizing this feature.

First, listen to be sure the frequency isn't in use. Then, announce your call sign and your intentions, such as "This is W1XXX, connecting." Let it drop for a moment, then key the rig again, and using the DTMF pad, enter the node number of the station. Drop it again, and wait for an acknowledgement from the system.

If all goes well, you'll hear a voice announcement indicating that you're connected to the remote station over the Internet. If the connection couldn't be made, you'll hear an announcement about that instead. Common reasons for not being able to connect are:

1. the node number you entered doesn't exist;

2. the remote link (or the local link) isn't up and running; or

3. the remote link is already in a QSO, and not accepting any more connections.

If the connection succeeds, you've opened up a two-way channel between the local frequency and the remote station. If the remote station is a repeater or a simplex link, you've set up a temporary "wormhole" between two local coverage areas in different parts of the world! During your QSO, it's helpful to try and visualize the communications path between you and the remote station. The diagram in Figure 1.1 is a good reference.

This will be familiar territory if you've ever used repeaters that are linked together by phone lines or auxiliary RF links. For the most part, you operate just as you normally would, making short transmissions and giving remote users ample time to reply. The only big difference is that there's an extra delay — for reasons that will be explained later — so it's VERY important to leave extra space between transmissions. You could say that the three most important rules are "pause, listen, and pause again."

You: "This is W1XXX connecting." (*pause*)

You: (*DTMF digits*: 1 2 3 4)

Link: "XX1ZZ Connected. Welcome to the XX1ZZ Node, serving Greater Hamburg and Radio Valley."

You: (*pause for 10 seconds...*) "This is W1XXX listening."

The Pause Rule is especially important if you're in a three-way QSO, with two stations on the local repeater and a third station on the remote link. When the other local station turns it over to you, wait a little longer than usual to give another remote station a chance to break in. And the Pause Rule is vital if you're participating in a larger group, such as a traffic net, when stations might need to break in at any time from anywhere. Nothing is more frustrating than connecting to a remote repeater, hearing a QSO in progress, but not being able to get a word in edgewise because the other stations are "picking it up" too quickly.

DISCONNECTING

When the QSO is finished, it's important to disconnect the link, unless someone else wants to start a QSO with the same station.

Although there are standard codes for disconnecting — for example, *EchoLink* uses the pound sign (#), and *WIRES-II* uses the string #9999D the node owner might have assigned special codes instead. Among other things, the repeater itself might have advanced functions that would be inadvertently triggered by entering a certain string of DTMF digits. Before making a connection, be sure you know how to disconnect afterwards!

OTHER COMMANDS

EchoLink has a special feature that allows visitors to listen to a brief informational message about the link. The standard code for calling this up is the star key (*).

A number of other standard *EchoLink* DTMF control functions are available. **Table 2.1** lists many of these functions, and the default DTMF sequence for each. Again, keep in mind that the node owner may have changed some of these to nonstandard sequences.

Table 2.1
Some Standard DTMF Functions for *EchoLink* nodes.

Command	Description	Default
Connect	Connects to a station on the Internet, based on its node number.	*num*
Connect by Call	Connects to a station on the Internet, based on its call sign.	**C**+*call*
Random Node	Selects an available node (of any type) at random, and tries to connect to it.	00
Random Link	Selects an available link or repeater (-L or -R) at random, and tries to connect to it.	01
Random Conf	Selects a conference server at random, and tries to connect to it.	02
Random User	Selects an available single-user station at random, and tries to connect to it.	03
RandomFavNode	Selects an available node (of any type) at random from the Favorites List, and tries to connect to it.	001
RandomFavLink	Selects an available link or repeater (-L or -R) at random from the Favorites List, and tries to connect to it.	011
RandomFavConf	Selects a conference server at random from the Favorites List, and tries to connect to it.	021
RandomFavUser	Selects an available single-user station at random from the Favorites List, and tries to connect to it.	031
Disconnect	Disconnects the station that is currently connected. If more than one station is connected, disconnects only the mostrecently-connected station.	#
Disconnect All	Disconnects all stations.	##
Reconnect	Re-connects to the station that most recently disconnected.	09
Status	Announces the call sign of each station currently connected.	08
Play Info	Plays a brief ID message.	*
Query by Call	Looks up a station by its call sign, and reads back its node number and status.	07+*call*+#
Query by Node	Looks up a station by its node number, and reads back its call sign and status.	06+*num*
Listen-Only On	Inhibits transmission from RF to the Internet.	0511
Listen-Only Off	Restores normal transmission from RF to the Internet.	0510

NUMBER, PLEASE

One of the difficulties with the node numbering system is finding out (or trying to remember) the node number for a particular station. I've tried a few techniques, such as yellow Post-It notes stuck to the dashboard, and driving around with the printed *EchoLink*, *IRLP*, and *WIRES-II* node directories — altogether about the size of a city telephone book — but clearly there *must* be a better way.

Perhaps in the future there will be an Internet Linking directory-assistance node, staffed by volunteers, complete with advice about local restaurants and attractions. In the meantime, here are some resources for locating node numbers:

• **Lists on the Web**. Each of the major linking systems has a Web site that includes a complete list of active nodes, with call sign, location, node number, and status.

• **Web search pages**. Several sites will produce searchable lists of Internet links that can be sorted several ways, such as by distance from a particular location. Some of these sites will also produce maps showing the geographical position of each link, along with its node number. You might want to print maps of a few areas of interest and keep them in a folder with your mobile station.

• **Personal lists**. As you browse the Web directories, make a note of node numbers you're likely to be interested in using in the future, and (in particular) the numbers of other nodes near you. You might find that the links you use most often are those within 100 miles of your QTH.

• **On-air functions**. *EchoLink*, in particular, has a feature that allows you to connect to a station by entering its call sign (or part of its call sign) using the DTMF keypad. It uses a system where each letter and number is designated by pressing two DTMF digits. See the *EchoLink* documentation for details.

• **Shortcut commands**. The node owner may have set up certain shortcut DTMF sequences for commonly-used nodes, perhaps only one or two digits long.

• **AVRS**. Although not yet in widespread use, there is a feature of the APRS or Automatic Packet Reporting System network called AVRS, or Automatic Voice Reporting System. This is a system that allows an Internet link to send a local beacon to announce its presence and status to mobile stations nearby. APRS rigs with receive-and-display capability, such as the Kenwood TM-D710, will decode this information and display it on the rig's front panel.

COMMON COURTESY

A repeater is very much a shared resource; and, in a sense, so is a simplex frequency. If you use a local repeater or simplex link for Internet linking, please be considerate. Here are some guidelines to follow:

• After connecting to another station, wait 15 seconds to determine whether there's already a QSO in progress on the remote frequency. This is also important when connecting to a conference server or reflector.

• If you used a DTMF command to establish a connection to another station, it's your responsibility to drop the connection at the end of the QSO, unless another local station wants to pick it up.

• Conference servers or reflectors are great for roundtable QSOs, but not a good choice for extended one-on-one conversations. If you run into an old friend on a conference server and want to carry on a 30 minute QSO, set up a direct connection instead.

• When linked to another station, keep all transmissions short, and leave plenty of extra space between transmissions to allow link repeaters' timers to reset. The extra space also gives others a chance to jump in and disconnect, if desired.

• In some situations (particularly on reflectors and conferences), it's important to key the mic for one second before you begin talking. This will ensure that all receivers tuned to link output frequencies have a chance to "open up" before the audio begins. If a tone-squelched receiver takes 200 ms to respond, a chain of *three* tone-squelched receivers takes more than half a second.

• Although operating procedures are much like VHF-FM, QSOs are often more like HF-SSB. The station you're in contact with might be 12 time zones away, in the opposite season, and not sharing the same first language with you. Remember this, even if some of the other stations in the roundtable are locals. When announcing your QTH, avoid saying something like "five miles south of the Park Street exit on Highway 42" — the locals might know what you mean, but to a distant station, it's meaningless.

• On *EchoLink*, avoid using remote nodes as if they were conference servers. For example, if you connect to W1XXX-R and find no one on frequency, but then get involved in a QSO with someone else who connects to W1XXX-R, drop the W1XXX-R connection and move the QSO to a direct connection. Otherwise, you're tying up the W1XXX/R frequency for no good reason.

• Don't leave a repeater-to-repeater link connected unless the stations using the repeater are aware that the link is active. For example, don't leave the link up and running for an extended period, unless prior arrangements have been made between the repeater clubs. Otherwise, stations in QSO on one repeater might not be aware that they're working through another repeater at the same time.

• If you're planning to use an Internet link for the first time, check with a local station first to see if there are any special rules or conventions for using the node. If you are planning a cross-country trip and want to use Internet links along the way, you might want to contact each node owner in advance to introduce yourself and learn about how the link is operated.

• Keep in mind that the primary purpose of the repeater is to extend the range of mobile and portable stations, and that Internet linking is secondary. Drop the Internet link if it is impeding local communications in any way. This is particularly important since a local station might need to break in at any time with emergency or priority traffic.

LINKING FROM THE DESKTOP

Some of the popular Amateur VoIP systems also have a mode that allows licensed hams to make an Internet voice connection directly from their desktop (or laptop) PC, using the PC's microphone and speakers. This is a good solution for a single, fixed user, since it requires no RF link at the originating end, and thus uses no additional equipment or spectrum space.

In this mode, you are shown a list of all available stations, from which you can make a selection and click to connect. Stations are generally listed with their call sign and location (or description). You can usually also exchange text messages with other single-user stations.

Figure 2.1 shows the main screen that *EchoLink* displays while it's running. The list of stations at the center of the screen is organized by location, using folders and sub-folders similar to *Windows Explorer*. The space bar works like a locking push-to-talk switch — tap once to begin transmitting, tap again to stop transmitting. The horizontal bar graph near the bottom is an audio-level meter that displays both transmitted and received audio levels. Other systems have similar screens and functions in this mode.

A convention adopted by *EchoLink* and *eQSO* is to identify RF nodes with a call sign suffix, either -L or -R, and single-user, PC-based nodes with no suffix. The -L suffix indicates that the node is a simplex link, and -R indicates a link to a repeater.

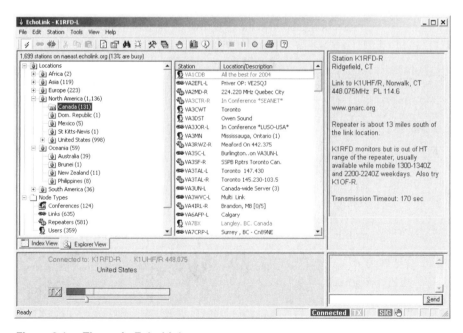

Figure 2.1 — The main EchoLink screen.

On *EchoLink*, even single-user nodes have an assigned node number, so they, too, can be reached via DTMF commands from mobile users working through a distant link.

If you are running a Macintosh computer with the OS X operating system, you can also connect to *EchoLink* nodes using a program called *EchoMac*, originally developed by Steven Palm, N9YTY. *EchoMac* is an open-source VoIP package designed to be fully compatible with *EchoLink*, fulfilling the need for desktop Internet linking for Mac users. It can be downloaded from **echomac.sourceforge.net**. *EchoMac* is based partly on a project called *EchoLinux*, originally spearheaded by Jeff Pierce, WD4NMQ, which brings an *EchoLink*-compatible client to the *Linux* platform.

If you're running *Linux* or a newer Mac machine, you might actually be able to run the *EchoLink* software itself. If you're running on a Mac with an Intel CPU, you may have already installed a copy of *Windows* using the *Parallels* virtual-machine layer. If so, *EchoLink* can be installed in the *Windows* virtual machine just as it would be installed on a PC.

If you're running *Linux* on a PC, you might have success using Wine, the *Windows* compatibility layer for *Linux*, which lets you run many *Windows*-based programs under *Linux*, including *EchoLink*.

Chapter 3

Conference Servers, Reflectors and Nets

We often take for granted one of the really useful aspects of radio communication: the fact that one transmission can be picked up by more than one receiver. Roundtables and traffic nets are a mainstay of ham activity. One person makes a transmission, and everyone else listening on the frequency hears it. Imagine how different things would be if every message had to be one-to-one, and sent separately to each station participating in a net. Aside from being extremely repetitive and time-consuming, it would be a tremendous waste of bandwidth, and be a huge obstacle to effective public service communications. After all, part of what makes Amateur Radio so useful for disaster communications, compared to cell phones, is its ability to get everyone tuned to the same frequency to hear the same message.

But the Internet is quite different. Virtually all communication over the Internet is point-to-point. The transmission control protocol (TCP) protocol, used by most Internet traffic, is strictly one-to-one; for each message, there is just one sender and one recipient. The user datagram protocol, (UDP) protocol, commonly used by VoIP systems, usually has only one sender and one recipient as well. Although UDP does have provisions for *multicasting* — sending a single message to more than one recipient — most Internet providers do not support it. If you have a message that needs to be "heard" by more than one recipient, it'll have to be sent separately to each one, somewhere along the line.

On the surface, this looks like a real showstopper for Amateur Radio VoIP systems. Does this mean that every VoIP conversation must be one-to-one? Are roundtables and traffic nets just impossible over Internet links?

Fortunately, there's a solution. A specially designed software package, called a *conference server, conference bridge,* or *reflector*, makes one-to-many communications possible over the Internet. As the name implies, a reflector takes in a message — in this case, a digitized voice transmission — and spits it right back out again. What makes it useful is that it can "spit" in many directions at once. The reflector keeps a running list of every station that wants to receive a copy of each message, and each time a message comes in, it sends a copy to everyone on the list, except for the sender (**Figure 3.1**). This way, every station that is connected to the reflector can hear what every other station is saying.

While this might sound horribly inefficient (and in some ways it is), it all happens in the blink of an eye, and quite automatically. Stations connected to the reflector hear every other station speaking in turn, just like an on-air roundtable, and might easily forget all the hard work that's going on behind the scenes.

One of the downsides, however, is that reflectors and conference servers use a lot

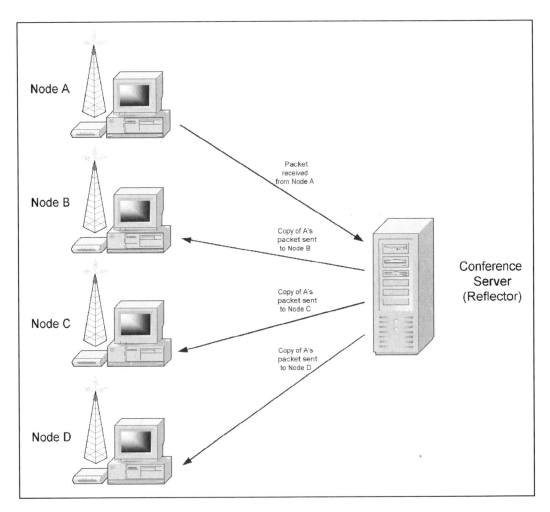

Figure 3.1 — A conference server sends a copy of each packet it receives to every other participating node. The conference server needs extra upstream Internet bandwidth, but the participating nodes do not.

of Internet bandwidth. If ten stations are connected to the reflector, every packet of data received must be re-sent separately to each of the other nine stations. For this to work, the reflector must have an Internet connection that can easily handle uploading nine times the normal bandwidth of a VoIP connection. Because of this, conference servers and reflectors are almost always connected to the Internet using big "pipes," such as OC-3 connections, which can accommodate the higher data rate.

Keep in mind that the reflector is doing all of the heavy lifting here. From each individual station's point of view, it's a one-to-one connection between the station and the reflector. Although messages (i.e., voices) from many different stations are being heard, they're all being relayed from a single point, namely the reflector. This means that a station participating in a roundtable conversation on a reflector doesn't have any additional Internet bandwidth requirements of its own.

In theory, a whole network of reflectors or conference servers could be interconnected to accommodate a very large conference, with hundreds of participants. The advantage to doing it this way, instead of using just one giant conference server, is that it distributes the Internet bandwidth requirements among several connections, instead of just one (**Figure 3.2**). Voice packets from stations connected to Reflector 1 are relayed to Reflector 2, where they are re-sent to each of Reflector 2's participants. If Reflector 1 has fifty stations connected, and Reflector 2 also has fifty stations connected, each reflector needs to send only fifty copies of each message to serve all 99 recipients. In practice, however, this is rarely necessary, since conferences of that size can become unwieldy.

On *IRLP*, reflectors are a prime meeting place for VoIP connections. There are currently about 20 reflectors available on *IRLP*. Each has a four-digit node number beginning with 9, such as 9200. The reflectors are generally named after their geographical location: the Alaska Reflector, the Indiana Reflector. Many of the reflectors support multiple *channels,* each of which can carry a completely separate conversation. You can always check the *IRLP* Web site to see the current status of all channels of all reflectors in the system (**Figure 3.3**). To connect to a particular channel on a reflector, change the last digit of the node number. For example, to connect to Channel 4 on Reflector 9200, connect to node number 9204. A special reflector, called the "echo reflector," records and plays back each individual station's audio for testing and adjustment. The echo reflector is node 9990. If you are setting up a brand new *IRLP* node, or moving it to different hardware, your first stop should be Node 9990 to be sure everything's up to snuff.

Recall that *IRLP* supports either of two different codecs: GSM and ADPCM. All *IRLP* reflectors support ADPCM, but by convention, GSM connections are usually supported only on channels 8 and 9 of multi-channel reflectors.

EchoLink also supports conferencing, in a similar fashion, but with different nomenclature. *EchoLink* reflectors are called conference servers, and have short, alphanumeric names that begin and end with an asterisk, such as *WX_TALK*. *EchoLink* does not reserve any specific range of node numbers for conference servers, so numbers can be four, five, or six digits in length. You'll typically find about 100 *EchoLink* conference servers online, many of which are devoted to a particular topic

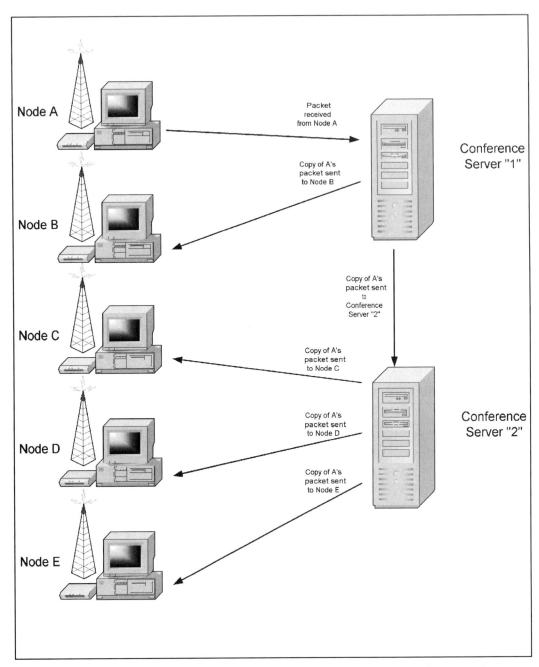

Figure 3.2: Two or more conference servers, when linked together, can serve a large number of nodes without requiring lots of upstream bandwidth at any single site. In this example, five stations are in the roundtable, but no single conference server is "feeding" more than three.

Reflector Summary

Reflector	Reflector Name/Location	0	1	2	3	4	5	6	7	8	9
9000	Vancouver			4		1		1			
9010	Discovery Reflector			2							1
9050	Interlink System Reflector	12	3								
9070	Alaska Reflector	12	1								
9120	New England Reflector				2		2	2	1		
9200	Crossroads Reflector		15	2						8	1
9210	Raleigh		1					1			
9220	openIRLP Reflector									3	
9250	Western Reflector	16					1			5	
9300	Saskatoon Reflector										
9310	Fredericton										
9350	LAX - [WALA] Hub	13							3		
9440	Internet2 Research Reflector	1									
9450	Dallas	2			43		9	9			
9500	Sydney - Virtual PUB					2					
9610	Great Lakes Reflector										
9620	Wisconsin Reflector	2				3					
9660	Micro-Node Reflector	4									
9730	Crossroads Annex			3							
9750	The UK Reflector						3				
9870	Denver Reflector			4	3	3		5			

Figure 3.3 — The current status of all IRLP reflectors is shown on the IRLP Web site at www.irlp.net.

or language. Some of the conference servers are interconnected as described previously. *EchoLink* conference servers run on an open-source package called *theBridge*, developed by Skip Hansen, WB6YMH, which runs on any of several different operating systems, including *Windows* and *Linux*.

An interesting feature of *EchoLink* is that the *EchoLink* software itself supports conferencing, so each *EchoLink* node can host its own mini-conference, bandwidth permitting. One nice thing about this feature is that two *EchoLink* stations that are in a one-to-one QSO with each other can "conference in" a third station without having to move the QSO to a conference server. Another benefit is that any number of stations can remain connected to an *EchoLink* node, in order to monitor it, without blocking out others from connecting. It's also slightly more efficient (in terms of Internet bandwidth) than using a conference server, since local RF users participate in the conference directly, without requiring an additional Internet path.

WIRES-II and *eQSO*, described in the next chapter, have conferencing features as well. *WIRES-II* supports a Round Table QSO mode, and *eQSO* is actually built entirely around the concept of conference rooms.

THOSE BLEEPING BLEEPS

When many stations are participating in the same conference, it's important that each node exercises good engineering discipline (and good operating practices). Part of this is making sure that the node doesn't transmit repeater IDs, courtesy tones, and other assorted noises. Imagine the cacophony of 50 repeater links connected to the same reflector, each announcing the call sign, date, time, and temperature every 6 minutes, even though no one is actually in a QSO!

This isn't usually a problem if the link equipment is co-located with the repeater. By picking off the repeater receiver's audio directly, instead of the audio coming out of the controller, none of these extra noises are heard over the Internet link.

But it's more of a challenge if the VoIP link is located at someone's station, away from the repeater. Here, the only source of signal is the *output* of the repeater, rather than the *input*, so suppressing the sounds generated by the controller is much more difficult.

There are four common solutions:

The first is to simply eliminate these sounds from the repeater altogether, and shorten the "hang time" to almost nil. Although this is usually easy to do, it tends to intrude into the repeater's normal behavior, and thus might not be too popular with repeater users who have no interest in the Internet link.

Another solution is to set up a second RF path between the repeater site and the node site. Typically, a UHF auxiliary link transmitter is set up at the repeater site, beaming the main receiver's audio directly to a matching UHF receiver at the node site. (These UHF rigs could also be transceivers, and used to carry the link audio in both directions, but it's not essential.) What makes this option attractive is that the node is working with the true audio path from the repeater's receiver, just as if it were co-located with the repeater.

The third solution is to try to suppress these extraneous signals within the linking software (or hardware) itself. *EchoLink*, for example, has a "Smart VOX" feature that will prevent noise bursts — such as squelch tails and courtesy tones — from triggering the VOX and being heard over the link. (This is described in more detail in Chapter 7.) But this is not completely effective if the repeater transmits other signals, such as a CW or voice ID, which do not resemble noise bursts.

The fourth (and probably best) solution is to use a sub-audible tone, generated by the repeater, to indicate the presence of a signal at the repeater's input. The tone generator is switched on and off by the carrier-operated switch(COS) signal from the repeater's receiver. This way, a remote receiver, such as the link radio, can use tone squelch (also called CTCSS, or PL) to determine whether or not the repeater is actually receiving a signal.

This is an excellent approach, since it usually requires no additional equipment. Many repeaters, whether or not they use CTCSS on their *inputs*, already have a CTCSS encoder available, so it's just a matter of wiring its control line to the receiver's COS output. Sophisticated repeater control boards might even support making such a "connection" in software. Making such a change is usually completely transparent to normal repeater users, who are unlikely to be using tone squelch in their receivers. The node owner then just needs to enable the tone-squelch feature of his link transceiver, and call it a day.

Of course, this doesn't *completely* eliminate the sound of repeater CW IDs, since the node is still using the repeater's output audio path, rather than its input receiver's audio. So a CW ID would still be heard underneath a station using a repeater, if the ID happened to come on during someone's transmission. But we will have achieved our goal of preventing the repeater's own ancillary signals from keying up the link when no one is actually speaking.

Suppressing these auxiliary signals is a good idea for *any* node, even one that never connects to a conference server. One situation that's especially important to avoid is ping-ponging between linked repeaters (**Figures 3.4** and **3.5**). If, at both ends of the Internet connection, the repeater's courtesy tone or squelch tail triggers a VOX-operated node, the two nodes will exchange "kerchunks" over and over again until someone steps in and breaks the vicious cycle.

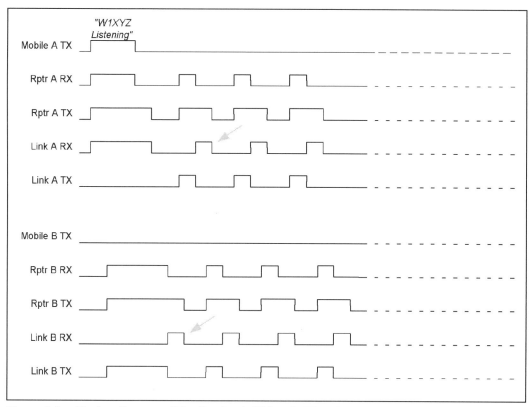

Figure 3.4 — Timing diagram of The Kerchunk Of Death. With Link A and Link B both improperly adjusted, W1XYZ's innocent ID sets in motion a vicious cycle of phantom transmissions, in which the two repeaters keep bringing each other up. The root of the problem is that both Link A and Link B are sending their own "tails" back over the Internet (red arrows).

NODE BLOCKING

To encourage the adoption of good engineering practices, and to prevent unintentional interference to others, owners of *IRLP* reflectors (and some *EchoLink* conference servers) enforce the rule that no extraneous repeater IDs, courtesy tones, and the like may be sent to the reflector. Nodes that do send these signals can be temporarily *blocked* from using the reflector, until the problem is corrected.

A listing on the **www.irlp.net** Web site shows the current status of blocked nodes for each reflector. If you're an *IRLP* node owner and you find that your node is unable to connect to certain reflectors, check this list to see if your node has been blocked. (Chances are, you will have already received a polite e-mail from the reflector owner, reminding you to double-check your system.)

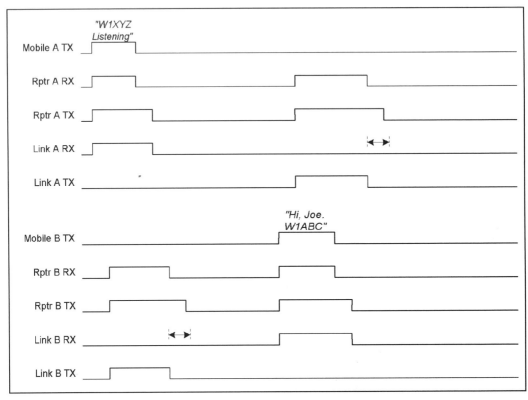

Figure 3.5 — With the addition of an "anti-thump" (or "pulseback") timer at both ends (red arrows), the problem is solved, and W1XYZ and W1ABC can enjoy a QSO. The timer begins at the moment the link PTT is dropped. During this time, the link receiver's COS is ignored. However, if the anti-thump timer is too long (more than a second or so), it tends to interfere with normal activity by clipping the beginning of each transmission.

Table 3.1
A Sampling of Internet-Linked Nets

Name	Time (winter UTC)	System	Node
EchoLink Help Forum	Thursday, 0200	*EchoLink*	6427
IRLP Int'l YL Net	1st/3rd Tues, 0100	*IRLP*	9000
EchoLink Tech Net	2nd Friday, 0200	*EchoLink*	6427
IRLP SKYWARN Net	Sunday, 0000	*IRLP*	9210
Visually Challenged Net	Tuesday, 2300	*IRLP*	9608
IRLP Swap Net	Friday, 0100	*IRLP*	9255
Handi-Ham Net	Tuesday, 0100	*EchoLink*	39980
Traders Swap & Shop Net	Tuesday, 0200	*EchoLink*	6427
Cleveland QCWA Chapter	Thursday, 0100	*EchoLink*	79637

NETS

Conference servers and reflectors are a natural fit for scheduled nets. Just as with FM repeater and HF SSB nets, Internet linking nets typically have a scheduled place and time, a net control station, and check-ins. **Table 3.1** lists a few examples.

The main difference between net procedure and normal conference-server procedure is that instead of working as a roundtable, stations are usually called upon to make transmissions by a net control station. As with other Amateur nets, a good net control operator is vital to keeping the net activities organized and the communications focused on the task or topic at hand. This is particularly important in the Internet linking world, where every connected station hears every transmission, and only one station can be heard at a time. Timing issues prevent stations from "breaking in" to be recognized, unless called upon by a net control. Nets can easily have more than 100 participating links, each serving a coverage area that could have dozens of stations tuned in.

Rod Templeton, VE7RJT, keeps track of *IRLP* nets, and manages a Web page with dates, times, and details. For the latest list, visit **www.irlp.net**. Topics range from local radio club gatherings to specialized modes (like SSTV) to swap meets. Each of these nets meets on one of the *IRLP* reflectors around the world.

EchoLink nets typically meet on conference servers, but can also be organized on nodes that are equipped for conferencing. The latter is a good choice for setting up a net where most of the participants are in range of a local repeater (such as a radio club net), but a few are checking in from the distant corners of the globe. Organizations such as Handi-Hams, local QCWA chapters, and youth groups all have regularly scheduled nets on *EchoLink*. Help nets, "tech" nets, and swap nets are held every week on some of the busier conference servers. Check the Calendar in the *EchoLink Yahoo!* group for schedules of some of these nets. Net announcements are sometimes posted in the *EchoLink* node description lines, and often also on the Internet, and are retrievable via a Web search.

One interesting feature of an *EchoLink* net is that you can participate directly from your computer, and thus have the benefit of seeing a dynamic list of the other net participants. This also makes the net control operator's job easier, since he or she can see nodes as they come and go, without having to do a general call for check-ins. For example, if W1XYZ-R appears in the list, the net control can make a directed call such as "Anyone on the W1XYZ repeater, please check in now." And, of course, if K6XYZ checks in directly from a PC, he can be recognized specifically.

Internet linking is still gaining acceptance by public service and emergency communications groups, and this trend is likely to continue. A natural way to gain familiarity with Internet linking and its role in emergency communications is to invite linked stations to check in to your local monthly (or weekly) ARES net. Or, if your ARES net meets on a local repeater, set up an Internet link between your repeater and that of another group nearby. If you do, be sure that your net control operator is familiar with Internet linking procedures, to ensure the net runs smoothly.

CROSS-LINKING

This book describes a handful of the major VoIP linking systems in Amateur Radio, and highlights some of their key features and technical details. If you've experimented with two or three of them already, the thought has probably occurred to you: Why not link them all together?

It's tempting to dream up "gateway" systems that join together two different VoIP systems, thus letting users on one system talk with users on another system just by entering a few commands. This is a natural result of hams' constant desire to innovate and extend.

But with Internet linking, there are some problems with cross-linking. The first, and most obvious, is technical. The systems have each evolved differently (and at different times), and thus use different hardware and software technologies and protocols. But the stickier problems are nontechnical, and have to do with operational differences — variations in the way the various linking systems are used, structured, and organized.

One specific issue in this second category is security. As you'll discover when diving into the details, each of the linking systems described in this book takes a different approach to bringing new users or nodes into the network, ranging from a casual online sign-up sheet to a strict procedure for proving identity. This can lead to concerns about one system becoming a "back door" for entering the other if the two are being interconnected, a situation akin to leaving the window of your house open even though the front door is bolted shut.

The bottom line on this is that you should do a little research before *cross-linking* your favorite VoIP systems (that is, joining them together) to be sure your cross-linked gateway will be appreciated and allowed by other users of the systems, and the system administrators who keep the machinery humming.

Chapter 4

Other Linking Systems

WIRES-II

Yaesu (Vertex Standard) has the distinction of being the only commercial Amateur Radio equipment manufacturer (to date) to offer a complete hardware/software package for Internet voice linking. Their product is called ***WIRES-II***, which is an acronym for Wide-Coverage Internet Repeater Enhancement System.

The package includes a specialized interface box (called the HRI-100, **Figure 4.1**) that connects your rig to your PC, and a *Windows*-based software package that goes along with it. New users must register by sending a registration form by mail to Yaesu; after processing the request, Yaesu will reply by mail with an ID number that must be entered into the software to activate it. This becomes your node's four-digit identifier.

Figure 4.1 — The HRI-100 in service at K1RFD.

Yaesu hasn't openly documented the technology behind *WIRES-II*, but it appears to be similar in principle to the other VoIP linking systems described in this book. The heart of the system is an Internet-based server system that Yaesu operates, and into which all registered *WIRES-II* stations connect. Once connected to the server, the software displays a sorted list of all other active stations on the network. Connections can be established either by keyboard or mouse commands at the PC, or by sending DTMF signals through the link radio.

Unique to *WIRES-II* are the concepts of a "Sister Radio Group" (SRG) and a "Friends' Radio Group" (FRG). A given *WIRES-II* station can operate in either mode. In SRG mode, up to ten repeaters and/or home stations may join together to form a Sister Radio Group for closed-network operations. This is said to be ideal for emergency, school, or sister-city groups. In FRG mode, any other *WIRES-II* station (anywhere in the world) can be contacted, as long as it, too, is operating in FRG mode.

The SRG mode sets up what is essentially a private network; only a small number of other designated *WIRES-II* stations can be a part of it. Besides security and privacy, one benefit of an SRG (and the magic number ten) is that any other station in the group can be called by pressing a single DTMF digit. In FRG mode, stations are accessed using six-digit DTMF codes.

SRG (**Figure 4.2**) sports an interesting feature, particularly for emergency commu-

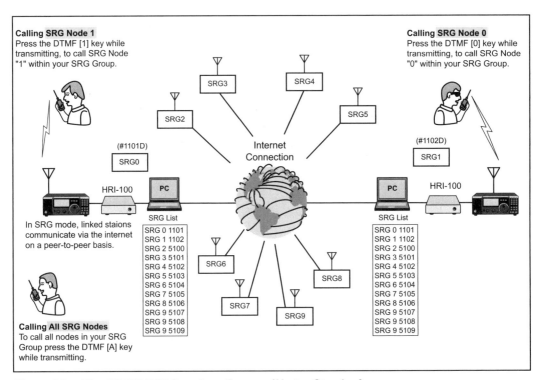

Figure 4.2 — The *WIRES-II* SRG system diagram. (*Vertex Standard*)

nications. The *WIRES-II* software can run in either the "Lock" mode or the "Unlock" mode. In the Lock mode, a single DTMF digit calls another station in the group, and the connection remains established until it's dropped, or times out. But in the Unlock mode, the DTMF digit is sent at the beginning of *each* transmission. This allows a mobile or portable station to selectively send a single message to a single *WIRES-II* node, sort of like the push-to-talk bar on an intercom. This way, a group of repeaters in nearby cities can be continuously linked with *WIRES*, but only certain *transmissions* are exchanged over the Internet, leaving most of the repeater activity local. This might be ideal for groups of busy repeaters that don't want to be part of a 24-hour-a-day conference, yet still want to exchange messages occasionally.

In FRG mode (**Figure 4.3**), a portable or mobile station tuned to a *WIRES-II* link can connect to any other FRG node by pressing the DTMF pound-sign (#), followed by the four-digit node number, followed by the letter D. To disconnect, send either #9999D or #99999.

As with other linking systems, the PC and interface box can be located either at a repeater site, or at any convenient off-site location using a link transceiver. A special interface cable is provided with stripped and tinned leads to connect the interface box to the audio input, audio output, and COS output of either a link transceiver or a repeater. (Yaesu even offers pre-made cables for some of its own FM rigs.) Miniature phone jacks and patch cords make the audio connections to the PC's sound card, and

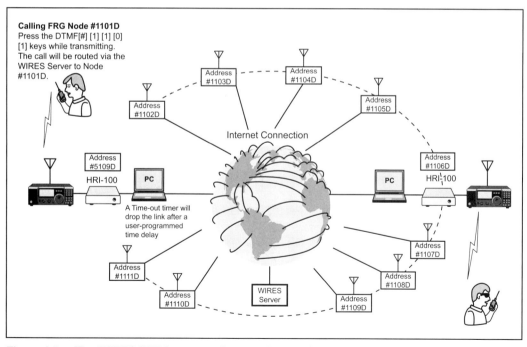

Figure 4.3 — The *WIRES-II* FRG system diagram. *(Vertex Standard)*

a serial interface cable goes between the PC's COM port and the *WIRES-II* interface box, to handle control functions such as PTT.

Either a dial-up or a broadband Internet connection can be used. In fact, the *WIRES-II* software can be set up to automatically dial into an ISP when it starts, and automatically redial if the connection is ever dropped. **Figure 4.4** shows the *WIRES-II* screen as it appears on the host PC.

Although the documentation doesn't specifically say it, it certainly seems that the PC used for a *WIRES-II* station should be dedicated to the task — don't use your home-office machine. The manual states that a large number of TCP/IP ports must be "opened" to the Internet (ten thousand, in fact!), and that Yaesu will, from time to time, log in to your PC over the Internet to do necessary software updates. The minimum PC system requirements are a 300-MHz Celeron processor and 64 MB RAM.

Several updates to the software have been released since *WIRES-II* was first introduced, each with significant new features. Product owners are sent an e-mail notification when a new release is available, and the new software can be downloaded from the *WIRES-II* Web site. The latest version supports features such as text chat and a Round Table QSO mode, similar to the conferencing mode of other programs. It also allows a picture (such as a QSL card) to be exchanged between nodes.

It appears that *WIRES-II* has achieved most of its popularity among hams in Japan and, to some extent, in the U.S. In 2008, approximately 1900 stations worldwide were listed as registered

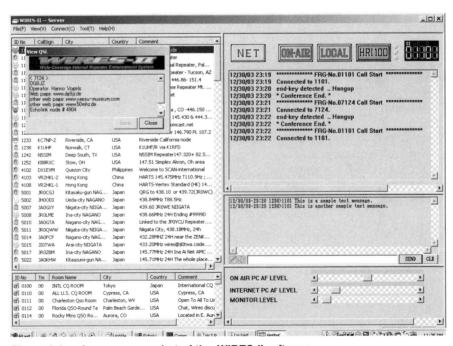

Figure 4.4 — A screen snapshot of the *WIRES-II* software.

with WIRES. Of these, about 74% were in Japan, and about 17% were in the United States. Of the stations actually online, nearly 90% were located in Japan.

For more information about *WIRES-II* in English, see **www.vxstd.com/en/ wiresinfo-en.**

eQSO

For several years, many *Windows* users have enjoyed an Internet linking program called *eQSO*. *eQSO* was developed by Paul Davies, MØZPD.

eQSO is actually a family of several different programs, for different purposes. PC Client software lets users connect to the system using the keyboard, microphone, and speaker of their PC. RF Gateway software supports interconnecting the PC with an FM transceiver or repeater, to operate a simplex or repeater link. Server software runs a conference server, in which any number of rooms can be created. Conference servers allow multiple *eQSO* stations to be connected to each other in a single conversation. Conference servers are roughly equivalent to *reflectors* in *IRLP*, and rooms are analogous to *IRLP* reflector *channels*.

The RF Gateway software (**Figure 4.5**) works with several different types of PC-to-rig interfaces, including general-purpose sound card interfaces and Internet Linking boards.

One significant difference between *eQSO* and other VoIP systems is that *all* communication occurs in conference rooms. In other words, stations do not connect to each other to communicate; instead, they each connect to a common conference room. Although perhaps less efficient for one-to-one QSOs, one interesting benefit of this arrangement is that *eQSO* is somewhat more "firewall friendly" than other systems. Rather than accepting *inbound* User Datagram Protocol (UDP) connections from the Internet, as other systems do, all *eQSO* users establish *outbound* Transmission Control Protocol (TCP) connections to

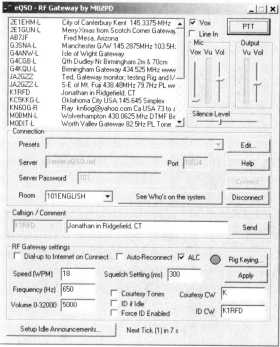

Figure 4.5 — A view of the *eQSO* RF Gateway software in action.

the conference server when they want to chew the rag. This simplifies firewall configuration (except at the conference server itself), since most home/office firewalls will allow outbound TCP connections without special configuration, yet usually require custom setup to support inbound connections. What's more, many offices and other institutions don't allow inbound Internet connections, for security reasons.

The downside is that TCP is generally less efficient than UDP for doing voice communication over the Internet, for a given payload. It also tends to introduce wider gaps in the audio when the Internet path becomes congested, and is more sensitive to latency, such as over satellite links. But over a clear, reliable connection, the results can still be excellent.

New users of eQSO must fill out a brief software registration form on the eQSO Web site, and send a scanned license copy for validation. The system administrators use this information to verify each call sign before access is granted. eQSO then e-mails a password and key code to activate the software. However, there's no stipulation that only licensed amateurs may have access to eQSO. The author of the program has made provisions for interested non-hams (Short Wave Listeners, or SWLs) to use the program, on the condition that they not transmit in conference rooms that might contain on-air links. SWLs are issued an identifier in lieu of a call sign for logging in to eQSO.

Administrators of *eQSO* servers do have the ability to control access by "muting," "kicking" or "banning" users that do not adhere to the operating guidelines.

In 2008, about 600 part-time and full-time RF gateways were listed on the eQSO Web site.

Since the client and server software are both freely available, it's possible to use *eQSO* to set up an independent, dedicated linking system of your own. With your own dedicated *eQSO* server, you have the option of permitting access only to a limited number of stations — such as RF links to a family of repeaters owned by your club — or "advertising" its presence to the ham community at large. The disadvantage, of course, is that the system would be unable to communicate with stations outside of the private group.

For more information about *eQSO*, see **www.eqso.com**.

D-STAR AND THE DV DONGLE

D-STAR is a digital communications spec developed by the Japan Amateur Radio League (JARL), and now implemented by ICOM in its line of D-STAR-compatible transceivers and repeaters. The system is loaded with features and possibilities, and has both digital voice and data capabilities.

Naturally, it's possible to link D-STAR nodes to each other over the Internet, using VoIP. One of the most compelling features of this kind of network is the ability to *route* voice or data transmissions from one Amateur to another, using only their call signs, without having to know in advance which nodes they happen to be near. A software package known as the Gateway Server connects a D-STAR node to the Internet, and a database of registered nodes and users, maintained by D-StarUsers.org, acts as a "trusted list" of members of the international D-STAR network.

D-STAR is partly an open specification, and some clever hams have come up with a little blue box called the DV Dongle (**www.dvdongle.com**). Among other things, the DV Dongle lets you connect to the D-STAR Internet network using a conventional PC or Mac desktop or laptop computer. The Dongle comes with a desktop software package called DVTool that lets you pick an active, registered D-STAR node from a drop-down list and establish a voice connection to it over the Internet.

SPEAK FREELY

Although not a linking system *per se*, Radio Amateurs might find plenty of good uses for *Speak Freely*, an open-source VoIP package available for both Windows and Unix.

The program's name was inspired by its ability to make "telephone calls," computer-to-computer, over the Internet, free of charge. It provides the essentials for setting up a VoIP connection, without some of the value-added features that a full-blown linking system provides, such as dynamic addressing and centralized security. It might be worth a look if you're considering a permanent, point-to-point Internet link, such as a dedicated inter-city repeater hookup. Since the source code is freely available, it's a prime candidate for a custom implementation if you (or someone you know) has skills in the C programming language.

The program was maintained for many years by John Walker, the original developer, and now can be found on the SourceForge Web site. The Windows version is found at **sourceforge.net/projects/speak-freely-w/**, and the Unix version at **sourceforge. net/projects/speak-freely-u/**. A variation on the Unix version, in fact, is the "engine" inside *IRLP*.

ASTERISK AND APP_RPT

Yet another option for Internet linking is to run the open-source *private branch exchange* (PBX) software package *Asterisk* with a special radio-linking application called app_rpt. *Asterisk* and app_rpt are discussed in detail in Chapter 9.

## Chapter 5

Setting Up Your Own Node

We've already pointed out that thousands of hams around the world have used systems such as *IRLP* and *EchoLink* without ever laying hands on a computer. Most of the major systems allow portable and mobile users to connect and disconnect the link using DTMF commands, so Internet linking is truly a two-way experience for mobile and portable stations.

But whether it's hands-on or at a distance, it always requires a computer-based link, somewhere along the way. If you live in an area not already served by a link, consider setting one up yourself! You might find that you already have most of the needed equipment, and the software is easy to get and easy to set up.

COMPONENTS OF AN INTERNET LINK

The basic components of an RF Internet link are a link transceiver, a computer, an Internet connection, linking software, and a linking interface.

Link transceiver: Although virtually any VHF/UHF FM transceiver can be used, consider using commercial-grade equipment for better reliability. For an *IRLP* node, the transceiver must have a "busy" or COS pin that indicates (externally) when the squelch is open. This can also be used with *EchoLink*, or VOX control can be used instead.

Computer: Just about any Pentium-based personal computer can be used for either *EchoLink* or *IRLP*. For *IRLP*, the minimum requirement is a Pentium-I CPU, at least 32 MB of RAM, a parallel (printer) port, and a Sound Blaster sound card. All of the necessary system software is provided on the *IRLP* installation disk.

For *EchoLink*, the system requirements are similar, except that a serial (COM) port is used instead of a parallel port, and a copy of Microsoft *Windows* is required. Avoid older editions of *Windows*, such as Windows 95 and Windows 98 — these are no longer supported by Microsoft, and may have serious security vulnerabilities when connected to the Internet. Newer editions of *Windows* are also much more stable.

Don't overlook the cost of electricity to run the computer. Remember that you'll probably want your node to be running 24 hours a day, 7 days a week, so the computer will need to be running continuously. I was shocked to learn (pardon the pun) that my own two nodes were costing more than $25 per month just in electricity usage!

It's hard to say whether an older computer or a newer computer is more power-efficient. Older computers tend to use less power at full tilt, but lack energy-saving features; newer machines use more power because of faster CPUs, but have EnergyStar-compliant features that minimize power consumption when idle. Interestingly, the best choice here might be a laptop computer, if you can find one with the right external connections.

Internet connection: Although a dial-up Internet connection can be used with either *IRLP* or *EchoLink*, a "broadband" connection is strongly preferred, particularly for *IRLP*. Most DSL and cable-modem systems will work fine. There is no need to have a *static* IP address.

Linking software: *EchoLink* runs on any 32-bit version of *Windows*, and the *EchoLink* software can be downloaded from the *EchoLink* Web site.

IRLP runs on the *Linux* operating system, which is available (for download) free of charge. In fact, a special distribution of *Linux* is provided on the *IRLP* installation disk. The *IRLP* installation CD comes as part of the *IRLP* start-up kit, which can be ordered online at the *IRLP* Web site.

Linking interface: All *IRLP* nodes use a custom-designed interface circuit that is provided by *IRLP*, as part of the start-up kit. This is a small circuit board that can be mounted inside the PC, or in a separate enclosure. The board connects to the link transceiver, a 12-volt power supply, and the parallel port of the PC. When mounted inside the PC, the PC's own power supply powers the board.

EchoLink works with any of several different types of linking interfaces, including some specifically designed for *EchoLink*, and others designed for HF digital modes such as PSK31. The interface connects to the computer's serial port. Some interfaces require no external power; others use an external 12-volt DC supply.

Linking interfaces are described in more detail later in this chapter.

PLAN YOUR SYSTEM

First, determine whether there's a *need* for a new *IRLP* or *EchoLink* node in your area. If there are already several simplex or repeater gateways for Internet linking, you might find that supporting an existing system is the best way to contribute. But if not, this is a great opportunity to expand the communications capabilities for mobile and portable stations in your area. Someone should do it, so why not you?

THE SITE

Second, decide whether the new node will be a simplex gateway, or a link to a local repeater. Naturally, a simplex gateway should be set up on a tall building, tower, or hilltop, to provide good simplex coverage. A repeater gateway, on the other hand, can be set up virtually anywhere there's an Internet connection and a good "shot" to the local repeater. Or, it can be placed at the repeater site itself. Either way, you must obtain the permission (and blessing) of the group or club that operates the repeater. The link will become a natural extension of the repeater, so it makes sense that it should be operated by an active member of the club that runs the repeater, or the trustee himself or herself, even if the link won't be set up at the repeater site.

If you're considering a simplex gateway, check with the local frequency coordination committee to see what frequencies (if any) have been set aside for Internet linking. Particularly if you live in a well-populated part of the world, you might want to avoid using popular "calling frequencies" for your link.

OPERATING POLICIES

Every Internet voice gateway should have an operating policy. The policy should address what times of day the link will be up and running, who its control operator(s) will be, how it will be controlled, and so forth. If you're setting up a simplex link from your own QTH, the policy could be as simple as "I'll be the control op, the link will be open to all Amateurs, and it will be available 24 hours a day." But if you're planning to link to a repeater, particularly one owned and operated by a club, it makes sense to work with the club (or its repeater committee) to come up with a suitable policy. It need not be written down as a formal document, but it should at least be agreed upon in advance.

The purpose of the policy is to ensure that the link is being used to its best advantage, without interfering with normal use of the frequency, and without violating radio regulations in your country (such as FCC rules in the US). It also helps ensure that the link is providing the emergency communications or public-service benefit it is intended for.

If you are working with a club or a club's repeater committee, a good first step is to offer to do a presentation at the next club meeting on the general topic of Internet linking, with some details on how each of the major linking systems work. A live demo featuring an Internet-linked QSO would be a plus. Be prepared to answer plenty of questions; experience has shown that many hams are aware of Internet linking, but have formed opinions on it (pro or con) based on incomplete, inaccurate, or outdated information. Your focus should be on how the proposed Internet link will benefit the club, the club's repeater, and the Amateur service in general.

Here are some common objections that might be raised:

"If we hook up our repeater to the Internet, won't that bring in all sorts of unlicensed non-hams?"

There is sometimes a tendency to think of the Internet as a mysterious, lawless jungle, with teenaged hackers "hiding behind keyboards" in darkened basements. In fact, it is simply a global communications medium, which can be made as secure (or insecure) as software and operating policies dictate. And it is potentially much more secure than Amateur Radio itself; Internet communications can be authenticated, traced, and controlled far more efficiently and effectively than RF communications. It all comes down to the security mechanisms of the linking systems themselves, which are discussed in detail later in this book. No security system is perfect, but still, you're likely to find that the greatest risk of striking up a QSO, with a non-ham, is speaking with someone who had just picked up a handheld transceiver at a local hamfest.

"How could an Internet link possibly help in an emergency? All of the phone lines will be down, so the Internet will be useless."

Without a doubt, emergency-powered radio equipment is the vital link in and out of a disaster area when phone lines go down. But that doesn't mean that Internet linking is useless in an emergency. Health and welfare traffic travels far beyond the affected area, and often, Internet access is still available very close to the scene of a disaster. Linking systems have already played an important role in the aftermath of natural disasters such as hurricanes, even when Internet access had been cut off to many parts of the affected area.

"Our repeater is busy enough as it is. Adding an Internet link will just tie it up even more."

This is a valid concern that should be addressed. Often, the best choice for an Internet linked repeater is one that has good coverage, but relatively light use. Sometimes, however, operating the link only during nonpeak periods can solve this problem.

"This all sounds fine, but it's not legal."

This is mostly a matter of operating policy and practices. In most countries, Internet linking is legal if the links are operated in a legal manner. Chapter 9 of this book explores this issue.

"This isn't ham radio!"

Whether or not Internet linking qualifies as part of Amateur Radio is bound to fuel many lengthy philosophical discussions, one of which you'll find in Chapter 10. (Undoubtedly, philosophical discussions are a *vital* part of Amateur Radio!) All other things being equal, however, it is hard to dispute the idea that a repeater with an Internet link is more useful than one without.

As the next step, try to gather answers to the following questions, to form a first draft of the operating policy. At this level of detail, it might be best to discuss these issues in a smaller group, such as the repeater committee or the repeater trustee:

1. Should the link be available 24 hours a day, 7 days a week, or are there certain times when the link should be disabled (or enabled)?

If the repeater is a busy one, you might want to shut down the link during morning and afternoon drive times, for example. *IRLP* and *EchoLink* both can do this automatically with the use of simple scripts. You could start by running the link full-time, and then see if it's necessary to cut back on its operating hours.

2. Who will be the link trustee?

The link trustee (probably you) will be the single person ultimately responsible for proper operation of the link. Unless it's directly connected to a repeater, the link will transmit under the trustee's call sign, typically from his own QTH. Usually, the link trustee is also the owner of the linking equipment, including the Internet connection.

3. Who will be the control operator(s)?

Even if you have determined that continuous monitoring of the link is not required by the Rules, every station (in the U.S., anyway) must have at least one control operator. In effect, the control operator is a person delegated by the trustee to keep the link in proper operation. Control ops should be hams who are thoroughly familiar with the system, and have some means for controlling it remotely, particularly if it needs to be shut down for some special reason.

4. Who should be allowed to send commands to the link?

Most linking systems have the option for stations on the link frequency to send DTMF signals to connect and disconnect the link. These codes are standard by default, but can also be customized in order to limit access to a specific group of users who know them. Should control of the link be limited to members of the club, for example, or be open to any ham who is passing through the area?

5. Should there be any access rules?

By default, the link can connect to any other station on the network, at any time. But, for a variety of reasons, you may want to block connections to or from specific stations. For example, you might want to prevent connections to another repeater across town, since linking two machines with similar coverage areas might be counterproductive. Or, you might want to inhibit connections to conference servers or reflectors, if the repeater is already particularly busy. However, avoid the temptation to limit access to the link so that only a closed group of stations can use it. This runs counter to the philosophy of both *IRLP* and *EchoLink*, which are offered to the Amateur Radio Service on the principle of open access.

Some of these questions are hard to answer before the link is actually up and running, since you don't always know what to expect. One way to come up with a good operating policy is to start with the "defaults," and then revisit these questions after the link has been running for a couple of weeks.

ORGANIZING THE SPACE

Next, think about where and how the linking equipment will be set up. The spot needs ample space for the computer and its keyboard and monitor, access to both the Internet connection and the RF gear, and a good source of power. Personal computers should always use a surge-protected power outlet, and an uninterruptible power supply (UPS) is also recommended.

Keep in mind that the link's computer can run in a completely "lights-out" environment. This means that there is no reason why the PC can't be placed in a locked, dark room, with no monitor connected to the PC. That's because all of the necessary functions, including software upgrades, can be performed through a remote terminal connected to the Internet. As long as you have the appropriate terminal software installed on your main home PC, you can always "call in" to your node's computer and do virtually any software-based tasks you need to do. However, a locally-connected monitor is recommended for the initial setup, and your PC's BIOS might insist on having a keyboard connected to the PC, even if it's never used.

RF GEAR

Then, consider what you might use as RF hardware. Unless the link will be co-located with a repeater, you will need a suitable FM transceiver (or transmitter-receiver pair) for the link. Some node owners insist on using commercial-grade equipment, but a dependable Amateur-grade transceiver can work quite well, particularly if it is operated at less than its full rated power. In either case, both the power supply and the cooling arrangements should be selected with long, continuous key-down periods in mind. Built-in CTCSS encode and decode is recommended, particularly for use with repeaters (more on that later), and the rig must have some sort of COS or BUSY output to indicate that the squelch is open. Many modern VHF or UHF rigs that are "packet-ready" have a rear-panel connector with a COS signal, along with line-level audio inputs and outputs; these are ideal for use with Internet links. If your chosen rig doesn't already have a COS pin, you might be able to modify it so that it does.

LINK ANTENNAS

Antenna systems for Internet links are generally simpler than those for repeaters, because Internet links aren't full duplex — there is no need to be transmitting and receiving at the same time. Thus, there's usually no need for a duplexer on a link antenna. As with repeaters and other FM stations, vertical polarization is the norm. If the link will be serving a local repeater, consider using a directional array, and operating with minimal power; for a simplex link, an omni-directional antenna with gain is usually desirable.

REMOTE CONTROL

Even if your country's Amateur regulations don't specifically require it, a radio or wireline control link is a good idea. If you (or your control operator) are always at an Internet terminal when the link is operating, you might not need anything more than the existing Internet-based wireline control link — you can log in to the link remotely to disconnect it, shut it down, or re-enable it. If not, an RF control receiver should be installed at the link site, tuned to a quiet frequency on a different band from the link transmitter itself. (In the U.S., an RF control link must be above 144 MHz, with certain 2-meter frequency ranges excluded.)

INTERNET CONNECTION

The computer you use for your Internet link must (of course) have some way of accessing the Internet. Not long ago, the only choices available to home users were dial-up accounts and expensive leased lines. Nowadays, in many parts of the world, "broadband" options are offered, and in many places, there is a choice among more than one.

DIAL-UP CONNECTIONS

Generally speaking, dial-up Internet service, using a conventional telephone line and modem, is the least attractive option. Dial-up connections usually are the slowest and least reliable of the bunch. If you have a clean telephone line and a good-quality, so-called "56k" V.90 modem, the top speed you can achieve is 53,000 bits per second (bps) downstream (*from* the Internet), and 33,600 bps upstream (*to* the Internet). In the U.S., the FCC limits the downstream speed to 53,000, and the protocol itself limits the upstream speed to 33,600. For peer-to-peer communication, such as VoIP, this means the very best dial-up data rate is 33,600 bps, since data is traveling in both directions.

But be careful! Your modem's connection speed, as reported by the computer when it dials in, can be misleading. Typically, it's reporting the *downstream* connection rate, which can be quite different from the *upstream* connection rate. Again, the actual throughput for VoIP is the lesser of these two figures. What's more, the effective rate can be diminished by noise or other interference on the line, and can even change in the middle of a connection.

This is not to say that there aren't many satisfied Internet linking enthusiasts who use dial-up lines. *EchoLink* fits itself easily into a 33,600 connection, and *IRLP*'s GSM codec works well over dial-up lines as well. But in many cases, the upstream speed is less than this ideal figure. What's more, dial-up connections tend to have the greatest variations in *latency* (delay from one end to the other), which can be very disruptive to smooth VoIP operation. Another problem is that noise on the line can cause the connection to the ISP to be dropped abruptly from time to time.

CABLE MODEM SERVICE

For a number of years now, a major "broadband" offering has come from the local cable TV provider. Many companies now offer Internet service through the cable system, using a *cable modem* installed in each household. This piggybacks two-way digital traffic on special RF channels, putting you and your neighbors on a kind of local-area network. In general, cable modem Internet service is an excellent choice for VoIP. Upstream speeds are usually 128 kbps or better, and downstream speeds are almost always at least 1.5 Mbps. The main disadvantage is that the service can slow down if many of your neighbors are using it at the same time, since the last-mile bandwidth is being shared among many subscribers. It also requires, of course, that you be a customer of your cable TV company, and thus might not be cost-effective if you receive TV service some other way.

DIGITAL SUBSCRIBER LINE (DSL)

Digital signals can travel a short distance over twisted-pair telephone lines, and many telephone companies (and others) now offer DSL service. This is a form of high-speed Internet service that rides over the existing telephone wiring to the phone company's switching center. In fact, it is usually possible to get DSL service without having to install a second telephone line, since analog and digital signals can co-exist on the same pair. A special DSL modem is required. DSL is also an excellent choice for VoIP. Although its top speeds are generally less than comparable cable-modem service, the bandwidth is fixed, since it isn't being shared with neighbors, so its actual speed may be higher than cable at many times of the day.

FIBER-OPTIC SERVICE

A fast-growing Internet service offering uses fiber optics, rather than copper cables, to bring signals to your neighborhood. If you're lucky enough to live in a neighborhood that offers this kind of service, take a good look at it. It features very high-speed Internet access, along with telephone and television service, all riding on the same fiber.

SATELLITE SERVICE

Several companies now offer Internet service as an add-on to satellite-provided television service. For many consumers, this is a third option for broadband service, and for some, the *only* such option. Satellite-delivered Internet service can work for VoIP, but check first to be sure that the ISP will provide you with a true Internet address when you connect, rather than a translated address (see the next section for details). Sometimes, this is available as an extra-cost option.

One potential problem with satellite Internet service is the high latency introduced by the long path between your ground-based dish and the geostationary satellite it uses. However, this is not likely to be a problem for VoIP systems such as *IRLP* and *EchoLink* that use UDP protocols, since these protocols use no end-to-end acknowledgement of packets.

FIREWALLS, ROUTERS, AND SECURITY SOFTWARE

In the early days of the Internet, computers could usually exchange information freely, simply by knowing each other's host name (or Internet address). Of the billions of possible Internet addresses, only a handful were in use, and virtually all of them were permanently assigned to specific computers.

Since that time, there have been two significant developments that have made the landscape more complex.

The first has been the increased focus on security. With so many millions of computers now directly connected to each other worldwide, there is clearly a need to keep the "bad guys" from breaking into computers remotely, or sending damaging forms of data.

The second has been the rise of shared IP addresses. As more homes and small businesses get broadband access (DSL or cable) as a replacement for dial-up, there has been a steady increase in the number of home/office computer networks, which (among other things) allow every computer in the home or office to share a single Internet connection. At the heart of these networks sits a special type of *router* that works as an Internet traffic cop, automatically translating the home's single Internet address to the correct "local" address of the PC being used.

Although these changes have brought benefits in convenience and security, they've made life more difficult for peer-to-peer applications, such as VoIP programs. These programs typically use pre-assigned *ports* to carry on their Internet conversations, and expect a direct path from one computer to another, rather than channeling everything through a central server. For example, *EchoLink* relies on UDP ports 5198 and 5199 being available at both ends of the path. This means that Internet users who want to use VoIP applications (such as Internet voice links) often must make changes to the configuration of their home-network equipment or their security software to let the VoIP traffic pass through.

Microsoft *Windows* applications are among the favorite targets of evildoers who create viruses and worms, and thus Internet security software has become a necessity on computers running *Windows*. Many of these programs, such as *ZoneAlarm* and *Norton Internet Security*, will prevent VoIP programs from working correctly, unless they've been specially configured. This is because VoIP software usually must be able to receive "unsolicited" data from a distant computer on the Internet, something that these products will block by default. The most secure work-around is to set up the security software so that it will allow the VoIP program to accept data on certain ports, rather than disabling the security software altogether.

Home networks can pose a problem if two or more computers, through a router, are sharing a single Internet address. Partners on the Internet can only "see" and send data to this one public address. So when unsolicited data arrives from the Internet, how does the router know which computer in the household to send it to? It doesn't — unless you've configured it to *forward* certain packets of data to a specific machine. VoIP systems generally use a limited range of UDP ports, and most home network routers can be configured to forward a certain range of incoming ports to a certain PC.

Unfortunately, if there are a hundred different makes and models of routers on the market today, there are a hundred different sets of instructions for setting them up. Most routers have a set of Web-based setup screens, but they all seem to use different commands, and even different terminology, for the various configuration options. Look for options such as "forwarding" or "server setup" in the router manufacturer's documentation. Then, check the firewall requirements in the documentation for the linking system you're setting up, and see if you can put two and two together.

One word of caution about setting up a home-network router: In a typical setup, the router assigns a local address to each of your home PCs using a mechanism called *DHCP* (dynamic host configuration protocol). This works fine for most applications, but can sometimes cause headaches for VoIP operation. Why? If you're running DHCP, the IP address of your node's PC can change from time to time, and so you might have to update the forwarding configuration each time it changes. DHCP has the idea of "lease" on each address, which is periodically renewed, but some PC's release their address when they're restarted. As an alternative, check your router's documentation to see what range of addresses can be used for *static* addressing, then set up each of your PCs to use a different static address in that range.

The *EchoLink* software now has a feature that allows it to bypass most firewalls by using a *proxy server* at another location. The *EchoLink* Proxy is discussed in Chapter 7.

LINKING INTERFACES

In the world of Internet linking, the device that sits between the PC and the RF gear is commonly called an *interface*, or a *linking interface*. In general terms, the interface performs the following tasks:

1) Routes audio from the link receiver to the input of the computer's sound card;

2) Routes audio from the output of the computer's sound card to the link transmitter;

3) Allows software on the computer to key and un-key the link transmitter;

4) Allows software on the computer to detect the presence of an incoming signal at the link receiver; and

5) Allows software on the computer to detect DTMF digits captured by the link receiver.

The first three items are familiar to anyone who has dallied in the HF digital modes, or otherwise used sound-card software designed for Amateur Radio. As described in the next chapter, the sound card is the critical "gateway" between the analog and digital worlds. The sound card does most of the heavy lifting, so the remaining interface between the PC and the rig can be quite simple.

However, effective Internet linking also requires that the computer begin "transmitting" to the Internet when the squelch of the link receiver opens up. So the fourth item above is needed, too. This can either be done by interfacing the COS signal from the receiver to a pin on the computer's serial or parallel port, or detecting the signal entirely in software, where the program monitors and reacts to the peak audio level from the receiver (similar to a VOX).

And since most Internet links can accept DTMF commands from mobile and portable users, some sort of DTMF decoder is required. Again, this can either be done in hardware or software. Hardware solutions usually use an inexpensive, high-performance DTMF decoder chip that connects to the PC's serial or parallel port. Application software can accomplish much the same thing by applying digital signal processing (DSP) functions to the receiver audio captured by the sound card.

The specific requirements for linking interfaces, and the options available, depend on the particular linking system you're planning to deploy. The sections that follow include more information about linking interfaces for *IRLP* and *EchoLink*.

SETTING UP AN IRLP NODE

To set up an *IRLP* node, you'll need the following items:
- Link transceiver with COS output signal.
- Intel Pentium-based computer, with at least 32 MB of memory. The computer must have a Sound Blaster sound card and a parallel port.
- Internet connection for the computer. A full-time "broadband" connection, such as a DSL or cable-modem service, is strongly recommended.
- *IRLP* interface board (see **Figure 5.1**).
- Custom-made cable(s) to connect *IRLP* interface board to transceiver and sound card. "Plug and play" cables for a few popular radios are also available.
- *IRLP* software.

Figure 5.1 — A close-up of the *IRLP* 3.0 interface board. The DB-25 connector on the right connects to the PC's parallel port. The four-pin connector at the top accepts the 12VDC power, and the 10-pin header at the top left goes to a DB-9 connector to which the link transceiver and the sound card connect. The board comes with brackets for mounting the board and the DB-9 connector inside the computer, or it can be housed in an external enclosure. *(Paul Cassel, VE3SY)*

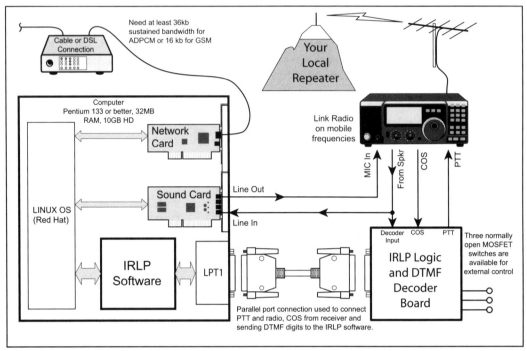

Need at least 36kb sustained bandwidth for ADPCM or 16 kb for GSM

Cable or DSL Connection

Your Local Repeater

Computer
Pentium 133 or better, 32MB RAM, 10GB HD

Network Card

Link Radio on mobile frequencies

LINUX OS (Red Hat)

Sound Card

Line Out

Line In

MIC In

From Spkr

COS

PTT

IRLP Software

LPT1

Decoder Input

COS

PTT

IRLP Logic and DTMF Decoder Board

Three normally open MOSFET switches are available for external control

Parallel port connection used to connect PTT and radio, COS from receiver and sending DTMF digits to the IRLP software.

Figure 5.2 — Diagram of a typical *IRLP* node. (Paul Cassel, VE3SY)

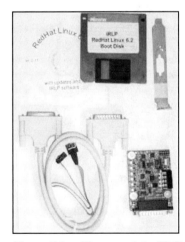

Figure 5.3 — The complete *IRLP* package includes all required software (including *Linux*), the interface board, and cables to connect the board to the PC. (Paul Cassel, VE3SY)

•*Linux* operating system software.

IRLP makes the process easier by offering a package that includes the *IRLP* interface board and a CD-ROM with both the *IRLP* software and a copy of Red Hat *Linux* (**Figure 5.3**). This is the recommended way to get started.

COS OUTPUT SIGNAL

The *IRLP* software needs to be able to sense the presence of an incoming signal from the transceiver. Basically, it needs to know the state of the receiver's squelch circuit — when the squelch is open, a signal is assumed to be present, and when it's closed, no signal is assumed.

This means that the transceiver you plan to use for your *IRLP* node will need to provide a DC voltage that goes from low to high (or vice versa) when the squelch opens. This signal is sometimes called

COS, for *carrier-operated squelch* or *carrier-operated switch*. A pin on the interface board's DB-9 connector accepts this signal and passes it along to the software.

With many modern transceivers, getting a COS signal is dead simple — a back-panel mini-DIN connector provides audio input and output, push-to-talk, and COS (sometimes called "busy"), all in one place. That's partly because these signals are commonly used to connect a TNC to the transceiver for packet operation. All that's needed is a single cable with a properly wired mini-DIN or DB-9 connector to make all the connections between the rig and the computer.

With other equipment, finding a suitable COS signal is more of a challenge. However, with the help of a schematic, you can probably find what you're looking for, and figure out a way to wire it to the interface board. The board can be jumpered several ways to accommodate the voltage and sense of the available COS signal.

INSTALLATION STEPS

1. Download an *IRLP* order form from the main *IRLP* Web site (**www.irlp.net**), and send it to the address provided.

2. Gather and prepare the necessary computer and RF equipment, including the Internet connection.

3. When the *IRLP* kit arrives, an instruction sheet will direct you to the last versions of the installation documents, which you can download from a special Web site. These instructions include:

- Information on how to install the *IRLP* interface board. This is normally installed inside the computer itself, as long as there's room for it (**Figure 5.4**).
- Detailed steps for installing the CentOS distribution of *Linux*, using the installation CD provided in the kit.
- Detailed steps for installing the *IRLP* software, also from the installation CD.
- Information on how to generate the necessary public and private keys for PGP, and how to submit the public key to the *IRLP* system.
- Instructions for how to test the node, and adjust audio levels.

4. Install the interface board.

5. Create the necessary audio and

Figure 5.4 — The *IRLP* interface board installed inside an HP Vectra PC at K1RFD.

control cables to connect the PC to your link equipment.

6. Install *Linux* and the *IRLP* software.

7. Configure the software.

8. Test the system, and adjust audio levels.

9. Submit the details of your new node to the *IRLP* Web site.

Once you are registered as an *IRLP* node owner, you'll be welcomed to join the *IRLP* Owner's forum on Yahoo. The archives of this Yahoo group are an excellent repository of information on node setup, adjustment, and troubleshooting. You'll also be able to download the *Unofficial IRLP Manual and Troubleshooting Guide*, a compendium of advice assembled from various sources (including the Yahoo group) by Jim Price, WW4M.

GETTING FRIENDLY WITH *LINUX*

One of the first pieces of advice for new *IRLP* node owners is to become familiar with the *Linux* operating system. *Linux* will seem natural to anyone who has used Unix, but might seem quite foreign at first to those who are accustomed to Microsoft *Windows*, or versions of the Macintosh operating system prior to OS X. There are several excellent books on *Linux* that are geared specifically to new users.

Although not officially a "flavor" of UNIX, *Linux* is a very UNIX-like operating system. It was designed from the ground up to run on commodity computers based on the Intel chipset, which means it runs very efficiently, even on the most modest of hardware. It also provides considerable flexibility in how it is installed. The version of *Linux* shipped in the *IRLP* kit is CentOS, a distribution based on Red Hat Enterprise *Linux*. Since it is essentially a "server" application (as opposed to a "workstation" application), *IRLP* has no need for a graphical user interface (GUI), so no GUI is installed in a normal setup. This means that virtually all of the installation, setup, and day-to-day control of the system is done with a command-line interface, rather than mouse clicks on a virtual desktop.

Although this may sound rather Spartan to those accustomed to using a mouse, it has two important benefits. The first is that it makes best use of the system resources. A GUI requires a lot of memory and processing power, so why install a GUI when it's not needed? The second is that it makes it easy to install *IRLP* in a completely lights-out environment. Although a keyboard and monitor are required for the initial setup, they can easily be disconnected afterward, and the computer moved to a closet or under a desk somewhere. As long as the computer has a reliable power supply and Internet connection, it is always accessible (and completely controllable) from a remote terminal running a console program such as secure shell (**ssh**).

UP AND RUNNING WITH IRLP

The steps for installing the *IRLP* hardware and software are well-documented, but do change from time to time. When you receive the *IRLP* kit, you'll be directed to a

Web site with complete step-by-step instructions on how to proceed.

For most installations, the only "hardware" steps are installing the *IRLP* board (usually inside the PC), and creating a cable to connect the link transceiver to the board. This cable carries the audio input and output signals, as well as the COS signal from the receiver and the PTT signal to the transmitter. Command-line utilities are included in the *IRLP* software package for testing the connection once it's completed. For example, the rig can be keyed and un-keyed by typing special commands, and the status of the COS and DTMF decoders can be monitored.

Figure 5.4 shows a typical *IRLP* interface board installation, as it appears inside the computer. The board itself occupies a back-panel slot (although not a motherboard slot), on which the DB-25 connector is mounted. A cable from the DB-25 connector plugs into the computer's parallel port. A ribbon cable connects the board to a DB-9 connector, which can be mounted in another back-panel slot on the PC.

Scripts drive most of the *IRLP* software installation and configuration steps. This will be familiar territory to anyone who has installed *Linux* or Unix software packages. The scripts create all necessary directories, copy files, and set permissions.

One of the steps you'll be asked to do is to create a *key pair*. This is a "public" key and a "private" key that are used in the PGP-based authentication process each time a connection is established. A particularly important step is to copy your key pair to a backup diskette, so that you can recover from a system failure, if necessary, by re-installing the software. Without a backup of your private key, you'd have to create a new key pair and register it with the *IRLP* system before getting back online.

Typically, there are only two adjustments that will need to be made to the software. The first is to set the audio levels on the sound card. The easiest way to do this is with a utility called *aumix* (**Figure 5.5**), which displays a set of virtual mixer controls as sliders. The installation guide describes a procedure in which you ask the *IRLP* software to generate a test tone through the sound card, and then use aumix to adjust the audio level into your link transmitter while you monitor the output with a receiver.

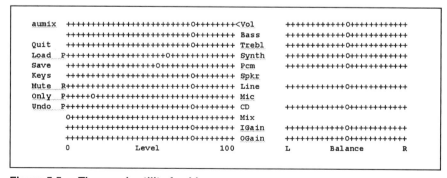

Figure 5.5 — The *aumix* utility for *Linux*.

The second adjustment is the *pulseback delay*. This is a feature that prevents the software from reacting to a false COS signal whenever your link transmitter goes key-up. On a repeater link, this can be caused by the link transceiver hearing its own squelch tail; on a simplex link, it can be a COS pulse coming from the transceiver itself. With the link transceiver set up and tuned to the chosen frequency, there's a utility that will key the rig briefly and detect and adjust the correct pulseback delay time automatically.

CUSTOMIZATION

IRLP offers many opportunities for customization, since the software is organized around a set of building-block components that are driven by scripts. For example, you can write or modify scripts to turn the link on and off at certain times, or respond to special DTMF sequences with control functions. Several useful examples of custom scripts are posted in the Files area of the Yahoo group for *IRLP* node owners. *IRLP* scripts are also discussed in more detail in Chapter 8.

One thing you'll almost certainly need to customize is the station ID. *IRLP* doesn't have a built-in provision for sending a Morse or voice ID over the link, so unless your *IRLP* gear is directly connected to a repeater, you'll need to set up some way for it to identify itself periodically while the link is in use.

A neat "trick" for generating a Morse ID without interfering with the normal function of the node is to use the sound card's on-board music synthesizer to generate a tone. The sound card's mixer will combine the Morse tone from the synthesizer with the sampled audio path, so the two are heard simultaneously over the link. To make this work, you can download and compile a simple C-language program (called *sccw*, for "sound card CW") that sends a string of Morse characters through the synthesizer with proper timing. Another downloadable script polls the state of the system to determine when the ID should be aired, and then calls *sccw* with your node's call sign at the appropriate times to generate the ID. With the right adjustments to the script, the exact timing and triggering of the ID can be set up any way you wish.

SETTING UP AN ECHOLINK NODE

To set up an *EchoLink* RF node, you'll need the following items:
- Link transceiver.
- Intel Pentium-based computer, with sufficient memory to meet the minimum requirements for the version of *Windows* you are running. The computer must have a sound card (or built-in sound device) and a serial port. If the computer has a USB port but no serial port, a USB-to-serial adapter can be used.
- Internet connection for the computer. A "broadband" connection, such as a DSL or cable-modem service, is recommended, although a dial-up connection can also be used.
- Suitable interface device. A number of different devices can be used,

including PC-to-rig interfaces designed for HF digital modes.

- Cable(s) to connect the PC and the interface to the transceiver. The interface manufacturer may have already provided these cables.
- Microsoft *Windows* (*Windows 2000* or above recommended).
- *EchoLink* software.

You can buy any of the commonly available PC-to-rig interfaces, or purchase a "linking" interface that has been specifically designed for use with *EchoLink*. Or, you can build a simple interface circuit yourself.

If you're inclined to build an interface circuit yourself, you may be surprised to learn that the most basic homebrew interface is extremely simple (**Figure 5.6**). You might even be able to stuff it inside the shell of a DB-9 connector.

In this circuit, the transceiver's audio output goes directly to the line input of the PC's sound card. The speaker output of the sound card goes to the microphone input of the transceiver, through a 20 dB attenuator. For transmit control, the RTS pin of the COM port engages the rig's PTT control by turning on an NPN transistor. That's all there is to it! To set up *EchoLink* to use this simple interface, use the settings shown in **Figures 5.9** and **5.10**.

This circuit is very bare-bones, of course, and assumes that you can get away with having a single, common ground between the two devices, without hum or feedback due to ground loops. One of the advantages of using a more complex, ready-to-run interface board is that most of these problems are avoided, since inputs and outputs often have DC isolation.

Examples of PC-to-rig interfaces are the RIGblaster models offered by West Mountain Radio (**Figure 5.7**), the Soundcard Radio Interface from MFJ Enterprises, the Tigertronics SignalLink, and the BuxComm Rascal. Note that these are soundcard-to-radio interfaces, not TNCs, designed primarily for HF digital modes

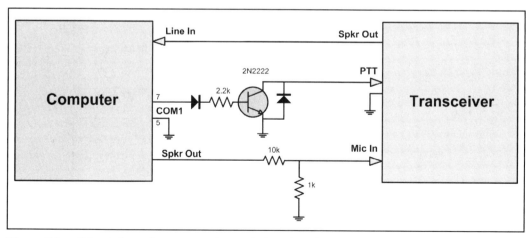

Figure 5.6 — A basic homebrew computer-to-rig interface for *EchoLink*.

Figure 5.7 — RIGblaster models offered by West Mountain Radio. These interfaces can also be used with HF digital mode software. The Plug-and-Play model also has a COS feature that can be enabled, which is useful for Internet links. *(West Mountain Radio)*

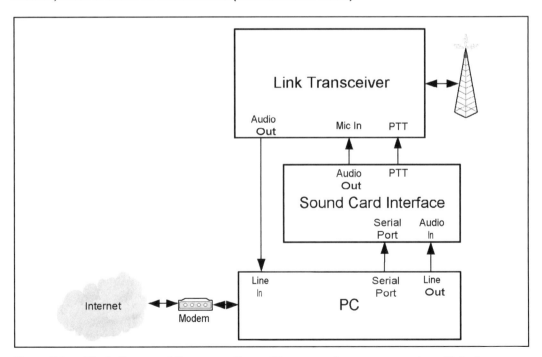

Figure 5.8 — Block diagram of the connections with a general-purpose sound card interface, such as the RIGblaster nomic (version with no microphone). This type of interface handles only the PTT and audio connections to the transmitter; the receiver audio goes directly to the PC's sound card.

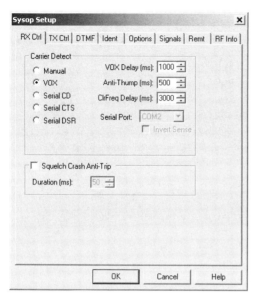

Figure 5.9 — The RX Control tab of *EchoLink*'s Sysop Setup, showing typical settings for VOX control.

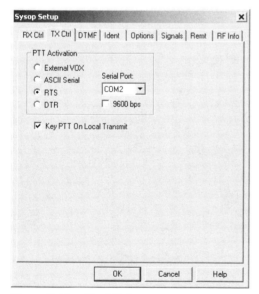

Figure 5.10 — The TX Control tab of *EchoLink*'s Sysop Setup, showing typical settings for use with a generic sound card interface, such as the type used for HF digital modes.

such as PSK31. They all connect to the serial port and sound card of the PC, and to the microphone input of the transceiver, and provide a way for the computer software to key the rig's PTT line via the serial port (**Figure 5.8**). When using one of these generic interfaces, DTMF commands are detected by *EchoLink*'s software-based DTMF decoder, and VOX is used for carrier detect.

Linking interfaces, on the other hand, have been designed specifically for VoIP software such as *EchoLink*. In addition to keying the transceiver on command, these devices have on-board DTMF decoders, and provisions for connecting a second receiver as a control link. Some have extra features such as auxiliary device outputs that can be switched on and off with DTMF commands, and extra connectors for routing audio inputs and outputs. Some can also be used with HF digital mode software, such as PSK31 or RTTY programs. Several models of linking interfaces are available from WB2REM (**Figures 5.11, 5.12,** and **5.13**), VA3TO (**Figure 5.14**), and G3VFP. The original WB2REM board was described in *QST* for March, 2002. **Figures 5.15** and **5.16** show the general hookups between these linking interfaces and the PC and link transceiver. An example of a more complex hook-up, featuring both a link transceiver and a control-link receiver, is shown in **Figure 5.17**. This example uses the VA3TO interface, but a similar arrangement can be used with some of the other types.

DIRECT REPEATER CONNECTIONS

If your node will serve a local repeater, you may have the option of operating the link through a transceiver tuned to the frequency pair of the repeater, or wiring the link directly to the repeater at the repeater site. There are pros and cons to each approach.

The main advantage of a remote link (i.e., through a transceiver located some distance from the repeater) is accessibility. The computer and linking

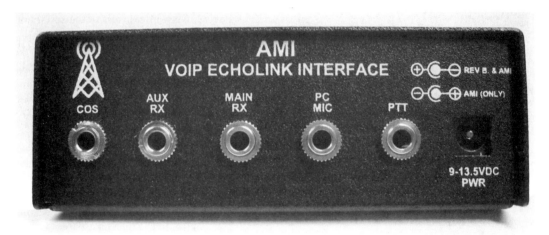

Figure 5.11 — WB2REM and G4CDY's AMI board in its optional enclosure. *(James Millner, WB2REM)*

Figure 5.12 — WB2REM and G4CDY's Ultimate Linking Interface, or ULI. *(WB2REM)*

Figure 5.13 — The ULI board in its optional enclosure. *(K1RFD)*

Figure 5.14 — The VA3TO board in its optional enclosure, with the cover removed. The matrix of solder pads on the left-hand side is a prototyping area where additional components can be added. *(K1RFD)*

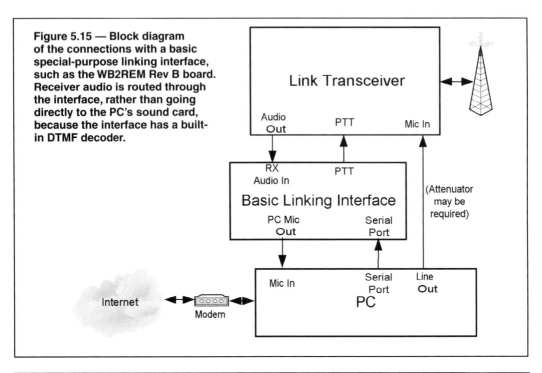

Figure 5.15 — Block diagram of the connections with a basic special-purpose linking interface, such as the WB2REM Rev B board. Receiver audio is routed through the interface, rather than going directly to the PC's sound card, because the interface has a built-in DTMF decoder.

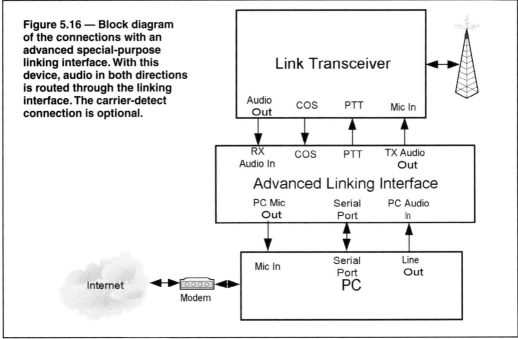

Figure 5.16 — Block diagram of the connections with an advanced special-purpose linking interface. With this device, audio in both directions is routed through the linking interface. The carrier-detect connection is optional.

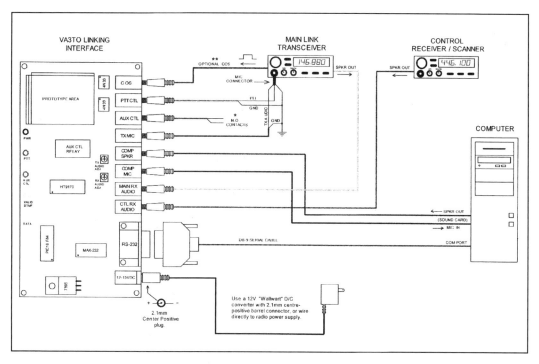

Figure 5.17 — A complete hook-up diagram of an advanced node setup using the VA3TO linking interface. The system has a control receiver in addition to the main link transceiver. *(Hugh Duff, VA3TO)*

equipment can be in any convenient location in earshot of the repeater, making it easier to maintain and monitor. It also might be the only option if no Internet connection is available at the repeater site.

However, some clubs have decided to set up the node at the repeater site, and connect it directly to the repeater equipment. The main advantage is smoother integration — the node's input can receive a signal directly from the repeater receiver, and there's no need for the node to generate its own ID, since it doesn't transmit its own signal. The link can piggyback on the repeater's emergency power supply, in scenarios where the power goes out but Internet connectivity remains. Also, in some situations, there are legal issues that make it impractical to operate the node as a separate station.

Connections between the node controller and the repeater equipment are usually straightforward. **Figure 5.18** is a block diagram of typical connections between a linking interface and a simple repeater system. The node is wired so that it takes its COS signal and audio directly from the receiver. On the transmit side, the PTT signal is logically ORed with the receiver's COS signal, but audio is routed directly to the transmitter, to prevent any DTMF signals received over the link from triggering control

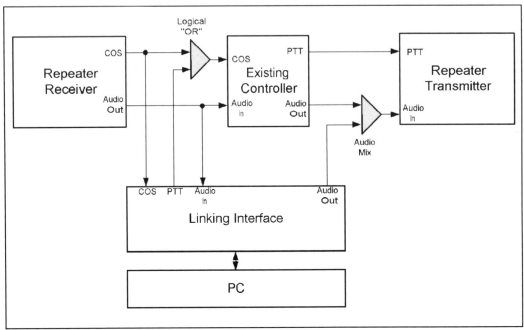

Figure 5.18 — A block diagram of typical connections between a node's linking interface and the repeater equipment.

functions of the repeater itself.

Some repeater controllers come with "remote base" connections built in. This simplifies the wiring, since all connections are made between the linking interface and the repeater controller. It also may allow the node to be enabled and disabled directly through the repeater controller using DTMF commands, either over the air or through the repeater's existing control link.

Clearly, it's important to choose reliable equipment if the node is to be placed at the repeater site. Just as you would select commercial-grade RF gear for your repeater, you should choose a business-class (or server-class) personal computer with conservatively rated components. Computers generate a great deal of heat, and the more rugged models tend to have higher fan capacities and larger power supplies. High performance computers are not required for Internet linking, so you might find a local business that is willing to donate an older machine that's several years out of date but still very reliable. For this purpose, an older 200 MHz machine with redundant power supplies and mirrored drives is clearly superior to a "top of the line" 3 GHz machine built for the consumer market.

Reliability applies to software, too. *Linux* has an excellent track record for reliability and stability, so you'll be in fine shape if you are setting up an *IRLP* node. If you plan to run a *Windows*-based node, the best choice for *Windows* is a version based on the

NT kernel, such as *Windows 2000*, *Windows XP*, *Windows Server 2003,* or *Windows Vista*. These systems also have excellent uptimes when properly configured. With a *Windows*-based system, it's important to keep up with the critical patches provided by Microsoft, which unfortunately are released nearly every week.

Reliable remote control of the PC is important when the computer is remotely located. Internet access is already taken care of, so the only remaining piece is software that will provide complete and secure control of the machine from a distant location. For *Windows* systems, *Windows* Terminal Services is available for server-class versions of the OS, and *Windows XP Professional* offers Remote Desktop as an option. You can also use a product such as *ControlIT*, *pcAnywhere*, or *WinVNC*. For *Linux* systems running *IRLP*, remote command-line access is available through **ssh** (secure shell). Ssh clients (such as *PuTTY*, from **www.chiark.greenend.org.uk/~sgtatham/ putty**) are available for several popular platforms.

## Chapter 6

Digital Audio and the Internet

SOUND CARD FUNDAMENTALS

The computer's sound card is one of its most versatile input-output (I/O) devices, particularly for Amateur Radio communication. But it's also one of the least well understood. In this section, we'll go on a tour of the innards of the typical PC sound device, and explore how it's used for digital voice modes such as VoIP.

First, I should point out that many modern PCs have audio capability built in to the computer, directly on the motherboard. Others have a sound card plugged into an expansion slot, such as a peripheral component interconnect (PCI) slot, instead. To keep the language simple, I'll refer to both types of sound hardware as "sound cards."

ANALOG TO DIGITAL, AND BACK AGAIN

Sound is reproduced electrically by using devices such as microphones and speakers, which convert audio-frequency variations in air pressure into varying electrical signals (**Figure 6.1**). A device called an analog-to-digital converter (A/D) produces a binary number proportional to an input voltage, and a digital-to-analog converter (D/A) does just the reverse. At its heart, the computer's sound card is simply an analog-to-digital converter that works at audio frequencies. In fact, it's both an A/D and D/A converter, since it can detect analog signals as well as create them. Just like any other analog-to-digital converter, the sound card converts an incoming voltage into a binary number, and vice versa. But since it's designed to capture and reproduce sound, it *samples* the incoming signal (takes a measurement of it) at a precise, periodic rate — an audio rate (**Figure 6.2**). So rather than converting a DC voltage into a single binary number, the sound card is measuring the voltage thousands of times per second, converting each measurement (or sample) into a number, and storing each of the numbers in sequence into a block of the computer's memory, called a *buffer*. Going the other direction, the sound card can take the contents of a buffer and convert each sample into a corresponding voltage at the same precise rate.

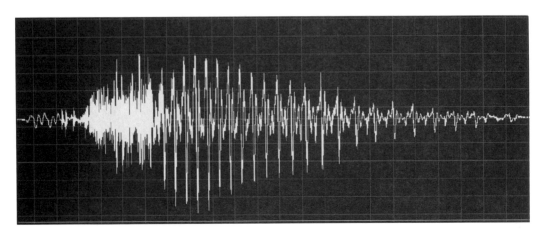

The letter "A"

◄————————— 350 ms —————————►

Figure 6.1 — A typical audio waveform.

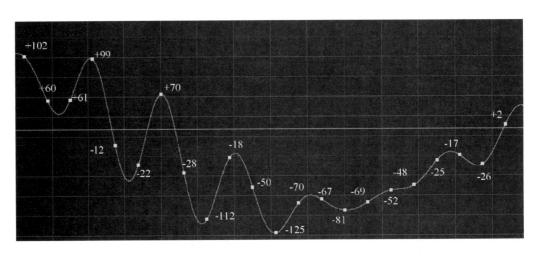

A small part of the letter "A"

◄————————— 3 ms; 24 samples —————————►

Figure 6.2 — Digital sampling of an audio signal.

What makes this extremely useful is that the sound card is converting an audio-frequency waveform to and from its digital equivalent. The more precise the measurement, and the faster the sample rate, the more accurate this conversion becomes. A principle known as the *Nyquist theorem* tells us that the highest frequency we can accurately capture is one-half the frequency at which we are sampling. So a sound card that is sampling at 44,100 samples per second can capture audio frequencies up to 22,050 cycles per second, or about 22 kHz — roughly the highest frequency most people can hear. (Dogs may wish to use a higher sample rate.)

Besides sample rate, the other important consideration is the precision (resolution) of the sound card's analog-to-digital conversion. Each voltage sample is converted into a binary number, and every binary number is a collection of bits (binary digits). Just as with decimal digits, the more binary digits in the sample, the wider the range of values that can be represented. A/D converters are said to have a certain number of *bits of resolution,* and thus, so are sound cards. Most sound cards can sample at either 8 bits or 16 bits.

The more bits of resolution, the greater the *dynamic range* — the difference in amplitude between the strongest signal the sound card can measure, and the weakest — and, similarly, the greater the maximum signal-to-noise ratio. With 8-bit sampling, there are 2^8, or 256, different voltage levels the sound card can measure. This works out to a maximum dynamic range of about 48 dB. With 16-bit sampling, the number of different voltage levels jumps to 65,536, for 96 dB. (Recall that since we're dealing with voltage, rather than power, dynamic range in dB = $20 \log_{10} R$, where R is the ratio of strongest signal to weakest signal.)

As with any electronic system, noise comes into the picture, and some sound cards are noisier than others. With no signal present on the input, you might find that the sound card is not producing a pure zero level. Since the true dynamic range is the difference between the strongest signal and the noise floor, the actual dynamic range of a given sound card might be somewhat less than the theoretical figures above.

Putting all of this together, we realize that faithfully capturing and storing an audio signal as digital data means using a high sample rate and lots of bits of resolution. Again with apologies to the dogs that might be reading this, we humans can hear up to about 22,000 Hz. Our ears have about 100 dB of dynamic range, and we have two of them. So to faithfully reproduce the sound of a symphony orchestra, we'd want to set our sound cards to sample at 44 kHz, 16 bits per sample, and in two channels at the same time (left and right, for stereo). As it turns out, this is exactly how an audio compact disc (CD) is recorded.

The bad news is that it requires lots of data storage. A 16-bit stereo recording requires 4 bytes of storage per sample. At 44,100 samples per second, that's 176,400 bytes for each *second* of high-fidelity sound.

Despite the noble efforts of hams experimenting with hi-fi SSB, the fact is that most radio communications systems are not hi-fi, by design. Usually, the important thing is to get the message through — and this means that *intelligibility* is paramount. Studies have shown that the frequencies 300 Hz to 3000 Hz are where most of the action is, in terms of understanding what the other person is saying. Not only that, but the audio dynamic range of most communications systems is a lot less than 96 dB. For these reasons, the makers of telephone equipment — the pioneers in VoIP technology — decided that an 8 kHz sample rate and 8-bit resolution were most appropriate for communications systems. This provides about 4000 Hz of bandwidth, about 48 dB of dynamic range, and requires 8000 bytes of storage for each second of audio.

There's a certain amount of psychology to audio quality. If you were to make an audio recording of your voice at 8 bits and 8000 Hz, and then play it back (using a program such as *Windows* Sound Recorder) through your computer speakers, you'd probably think that it sounded terribly "narrow" and tinny, especially compared to one of the higher sample rates. But try the same experiment listening to the results over a 2-meter simplex frequency. You'll probably discover that the sound coming from your handheld transceiver is just fine, and that it sounds more like a live transmission than a recording. And most importantly, you'll probably understand every single word quite clearly.

COMPRESSION

A stream of digital audio sampled at 8 bits, 8000 Hz requires 8000 bytes of storage per second. This means it can be transmitted from one computer to another at a minimum rate of 8000 bytes per second, or 64,000 bits per second, without needing extra time to "catch up." In this example, 64,000 bits per second, or roughly 64 kilobits per second, is the *data rate* of the digital signal from one computer to another. If the signal is moving over a single pair of wires, such as a telephone line or an Internet connection, you'd expect that the connection would need to have a *bandwidth* of 64 kHz.

Fortunately, mathematicians and computer scientists have figured out ways to do more with less. Bandwidth is expensive, so it would be cheaper and more practical to squeeze this same digital signal through a narrower "pipe." One of the most effective techniques for doing this is *compression*.

Compression is the art and science of squeezing a long stream of bits down to a shorter stream by taking out repetitive information. My wife never fails to remind me when I begin telling her the same story twice. When I begin to see her eyes roll, I know she's already heard it. So instead, I could give each of my jokes and stories a number, and just say "Honey, 4552!" This would save a lot of unnecessary bandwidth. (She still wouldn't laugh, but at least we'd avoid the rolling pupils.)

The same holds true for digital information. A computer can be programmed to look for repeating patterns in the signal, such as frequently used words, and substitute each with a much shorter digital abbreviation. The opposite task, *decompression*, involves putting the signal back the way it was by reversing this procedure. All of this takes a little more processing power at both ends, but can often save a lot of bandwidth. The difference in size between the original signal and the compressed signal is called the *compression ratio*.

Table 6.1
Common audio sample rates.

Sample Rate	Bandwidth	Typical Application
44 kHz	22 kHz	CD-quality music
22 kHz	11 kHz	Radio-quality music
11 kHz	5.5 kHz	Radio-quality voice
8 kHz	4 kHz	Two-way voice communications

LESS IS MORE

There are two flavors of compression, for different purposes: *lossy* and *lossless*. With lossless compression, the decompressed signal is identical to the original — no information is lost. With lossy compression, the decompressed signal is a little different — something has become lost in the translation.

So why be lossy when you can be lossless? It depends on the kind of information being processed. If it's a financial spreadsheet, every digit and decimal point is important, so lossless is the only way to go. But if it's a representation of something we see or hear, we can easily afford to lose some information, if it's a detail we'd never notice. And the big benefit of lossy compression is that it can give us much better compression ratios.

If you've ever worked with a digital camera, you've probably heard of the JPEG file format. JPEG files use an ingenious type of lossy compression that's specially designed for photographic images. By removing certain details that the human eye doesn't notice, an enormous number of bytes can be saved.

The same idea applies to audio data. Special compression techniques can be applied to a digital audio signal to remove unimportant information, yielding a decompressed version that sounds almost the same as the original, and again saving lots of bytes in transit.

A computer program that compresses and decompresses data is called a *codec* (an abbreviation for compressor-decompressor). Frequently, audio codecs are designed to work with signals with a specific sample rate. For example, *EchoLink* uses the GSM (Global System for Mobile Communications) codec, which squeezes an 8-bit, 8000 Hz signal from 64,000 bits per second down to 13,200 bits per second. This makes it possible to send a GSM-compressed audio signal over a narrowband connection, such as a conventional telephone line with a dial-up modem at each end. Another example is ADPCM (adaptive differential pulse-code modulation), which works at any of several different sample rates, and provides less compression, but generally better audio quality. *EchoLink* uses GSM, and *IRLP* can use either ADPCM or GSM.

STREAMING AUDIO AND THE INTERNET

There's been plenty of talk recently about *streaming* audio and video over the Internet. Streaming audio is at the heart of a VoIP system. But what exactly does it mean?

To explain, let's begin with some background on how information moves from one place to another over the Internet. An Internet connection can actually use any of several *protocols* to transfer data. The one most commonly used is TCP, or Transmission Control Protocol. When two computers are exchanging data using TCP, they are said to be *connected* over a TCP *session*.

The "connection" between the two computers, in this sense, is really just an abstraction. But it's a powerful concept. When a TCP session has been established, a program on one machine can send data to a program on the other machine, and be assured that the message will arrive exactly as it was sent, with no loss of information, no matter how big the message is, or what kind of data it contains. This assurance is known as *guaranteed delivery*. It's the same "guarantee" that an Amateur packet network makes when two stations connect using AX.25. In essence, TCP allows the two machines to set up a temporary, virtual circuit, over which information can be reliably transferred.

Although TCP guarantees the delivery of the message (as long as the virtual circuit isn't interrupted), it makes no guarantees as to how long it will take to transmit it. Over a clean, fat pipe, it could take a fraction of a second. Over a thin, noisy circuit, it could take a lot longer, because so few of the packets arrive at their destination intact — TCP retransmits them until all have been verified.

This is great for certain kinds of messages, like e-mail messages and (to some extent) Web pages. We're willing to wait a couple of extra seconds for these messages to arrive at their destination intact. But it poses a dilemma for real-time data, such as audio, which has to arrive *promptly* at its destination, and with a predictable delay. If you speak the word "radio," imagine what would happen if the word was split into three packets — one for each syllable — and the "ray" and the "dee" made it across almost instantly, but the "oh" was delayed by a couple of seconds. It would introduce either a two-second gap between syllables, or a two-second delay for the whole word.

The problem lies in the fact that the Internet, at its basic protocol level, makes no guarantees about whether a packet will arrive, or when, or even in what order. This presents a serious challenge for real-time audio and video applications, for which time is of the essence. These applications are sometimes called *isochronous*, since they must process regular amounts of data at fixed intervals. The best kind of network for streaming audio and video is one that has a fixed amount of *latency*, or delay, from one end to the other. Unfortunately, this isn't generally true of the Internet.

To meet the challenge, there's another commonly used Internet protocol called User Datagram Protocol, or UDP. Unlike TCP, UDP is "unconnected" — there is no virtual circuit between peers, and no implicit guarantees about how packets will be delivered. The only guarantee is that errors can be detected, so the receiver can ignore any packets that arrive garbled. It's analogous to the AX.25 UI frames used by APRS.

How does this improve the landscape for real-time audio and video? Unlike TCP, UDP has no built-in handshaking or acknowledgement mechanism. Packets are sent from one computer to the other in fire-and-forget fashion. If a given packet doesn't arrive at its destination, neither the sender nor the receiver is any the wiser. This significantly reduces the overhead of acknowledgements and re-tries, and makes the latency more predictable. With UDP, the only thing getting in the way of seeing a nice, even stream of packets at the other end is the variability of the Internet itself.

But hold on a second — if UDP doesn't guarantee that each packet will get delivered, doesn't this mean that the receiver might miss some parts of the message? Absolutely. But this is an acceptable trade-off for audio and video applications, which are normally intended for consumption by human eyes and ears. Just as lossy compression is an acceptable trade-off for squeezing the size of an audio data stream, so is the non-guaranteed nature of UDP. When we stream data using UDP, we're saying, "It's better to miss a syllable here and there, than to wait a long time for the message to get through, just because a couple of syllables were missed."

THE JITTER BUG

I hinted earlier that the latency of the Internet is unpredictable. If Computer A sends two UDP packets to Computer B over the Internet, the first one might take 50 milliseconds to arrive, and the second one might take 5000 milliseconds to arrive. The most common reason for the extra delay is simply network congestion; somewhere along the line, a buffer gets temporarily backlogged with packets to send.

Variations in latency are often called *jitter.* Compare **Figures 6.3** and **6.4**. For

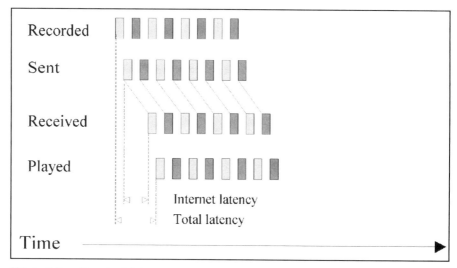

Figure 6.3 — Constant latency.

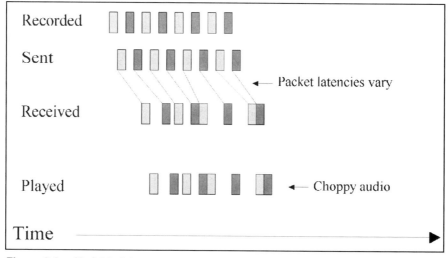

Figure 6.4 — Variable latency.

streaming audio to work smoothly, the system needs to have a way to compensate for jitter. This is usually done at the receiving end, since the fire-and-forget sender rarely knows how long packets are taking to arrive. And, it's usually done using a memory structure called a *buffer*.

Let's return to the checkout line in the supermarket. I take the items out of the cart and put them on the conveyor belt; the cashier, working from the other end of the belt, scans them and tosses them in bags. Naturally, however, the cashier does his job a lot more smoothly than I do mine. While I struggle to lift the extra-large jug of Dreft from the bottom of the cart, and explain to my daughter why the jumbo Butterfinger on the candy rack would not be a wise purchase, the cashier is scanning item after item like clockwork. How is this possible?

The answer, of course, is the conveyor belt. It doesn't make anything go faster, but it sure does make things go more smoothly. Even though I'm putting items on the belt at various different rates, the cashier is scanning them at a smooth two items per second. As long as my average rate is at least two items per second, and there are always some items waiting in line on the belt, the cashier never has to wait for me. I have lots of jitter, but the cashier never notices it.

Computer software for receiving streaming audio usually has a digital "conveyor belt" built into it. This is certainly the case with Internet linking systems such as *EchoLink* and *IRLP*. This jitter compensation buffer is a queue, which fills up with incoming UDP packets at one end, and empties them into the sound card (or codec) from the other. The queue is large enough that it can compensate for most variations in latency, but small enough that it doesn't introduce too much extra delay (**Figure 6.5**). As you can see, this is a trade-off, and it is usually adjustable.

Besides smoothing out jitter, there's another benefit to having this buffer. Recall

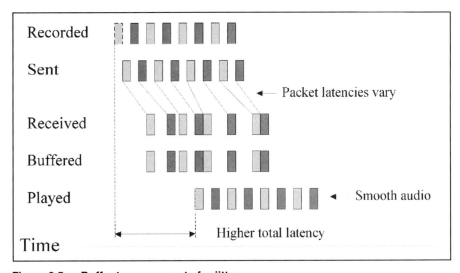

Figure 6.5 — Buffer to compensate for jitter.

that UDP makes no guarantee about whether packets will ever arrive, or in what order. In fact, it doesn't even guarantee that the receiver won't get duplicate packets. To help the receiver detect these problems, a program that sends streaming audio usually marks each successive packet with a serial number or a timestamp. Then, when packets arrive at the receiver, the receiver can try to ensure that they are placed in the buffer in the correct order. If packet 123 arrives just ahead of packet 122, the packets can be reordered in the buffer. Similarly, if two copies of packet 123 arrive, the receiver can detect it by seeing that it already has a copy of 123 in its buffer.

The receiver can also detect missing packets. If 122, 123, and 125 arrive, but 124 never does, it will be quite evident when the receiver pulls 123 from the buffer, sends it to the sound card, and then notices that next in line is 125. At this point, the receiver might want to insert a blank (or duplicate) packet to take the place of the AWOL 124, to ensure that the timing doesn't suffer.

STAYING IN SYNC

Now that we've addressed the problem of jitter, there's another problem to contend with. It's the problem of synchronization.

The sending computer is sampling an audio signal at 8000 samples per second, compressing the data, and transmitting it over the Internet to the receiver. The receiver is accepting this data, decompressing it, and converting it back to an analog signal, also at 8000 samples per second. Everything is working well.

But what if the sender's sound card is actually running at 7920 samples per second, instead of exactly 8000 — one percent slower (**Figure 6.6**)? It means that the receiver's

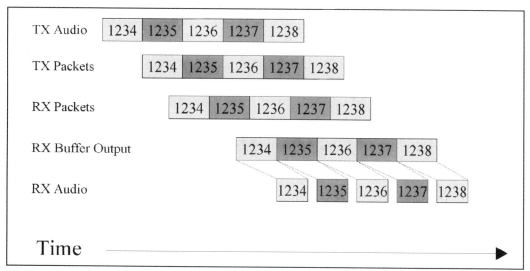

Figure 6.6 — Timing mismatch: Sender running slower than receiver.

card is running slightly faster by comparison, and thus will eventually become starved for data — the sender won't be feeding it packets fast enough, and sooner or later, the digital conveyor belt will become empty. Unless we do something about it, we'll start hearing gaps in the audio.

It seems like a minor mismatch (only one percent), but if you work out the math, you'll see it can be a real problem. If we're sending 12.5 packets per second, each packet contains 640 samples. If the sender is running 80 samples per second slower than the receiver, it means the receiver will fall behind at the rate of one packet every 8 seconds. If the jitter buffer normally holds 500 ms worth of data (about 6 packets), the buffer will be completely empty after 48 seconds, well within the duration of a typical transmission.

The opposite situation can be a problem, too. If the sender is running faster than the receiver, the receiver's buffer will start to get bigger and bigger (**Figure 6.7**). Assuming there's plenty of memory, the total delay from sender to receiver will start to grow, making it extremely difficult to carry on a two-way conversation.

Although most sound cards are crystal-controlled, there seems to be a wide variation in their actual sample rates when they are asked to operate at the nominal rate of 8000 Hz. This may be due to the architecture of the individual cards, particularly the way the crystal frequency is divided down to produce the actual codec clock. Spot-check testing has shown that some cards are off by as much as two percent.

There are several ways to address this problem. The most obvious is to adjust the sample rate of the receiver's sound card so it's exactly in tune with the average rate at which packets are arriving from the sender. However, many sound cards do not

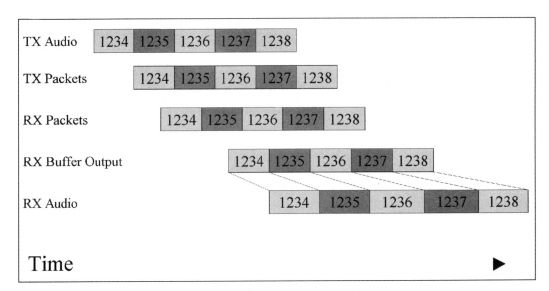

Figure 6.7 — Timing mismatch: Sender running faster than receiver.

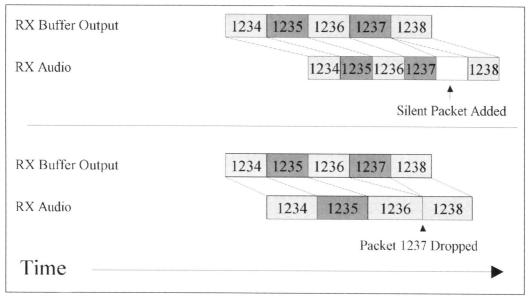

Figure 6.8 — Compensating for timing differences by adding or removing packets.

allow this kind of fine-tuning, so it's not a universal solution. Another approach is to use DSP (Digital Signal Processing) functions to convert the sender's sample rate to the receiver's sample rate, in effect, doing the fine-tuning in software. That may be computationally intensive, and might introduce unpleasant artifacts in the recovered audio.

A compromise solution is to make the adjustments by adding or removing entire packets. This is the approach used by *EchoLink* (**Figure 6.8**). The receiver's software keeps an eye on the average size of the jitter buffer. If the buffer seems to be consistently shrinking in size over time, it will insert an extra packet of silence to compensate for it. If, however, the buffer seems to be growing over time, it pulls a packet out of it. This technique is fully self-adjusting, since the act of adding or removing a packet immediately returns the buffer to its normal size, after which the process begins all over again.

How does this sound at the receiving end? If the sender is running one percent slower than the receiver, you'll hear a very brief gap of silence once every 48 seconds. If the sender is running one percent faster, you'll hear a slight stutter once every 48 seconds. In between those times, the audio should sound smooth and relatively normal, except that the pitch of the speaker's voice will be a little higher or lower than it should be.

ARCHITECTURE OF A SOUND CARD

A typical sound card is actually a combination of several devices: a waveform device, a musical synthesizer, a MIDI interface, and a pair of mixers. We'll focus on the two devices that are relevant to VoIP systems: the waveform device and the mixers.

CATCH THE WAVE!

As we've already discussed, the waveform device captures digital samples of analog sound signals, and (in reverse) produces analog sound signals from digital samples. This is sometimes just called the *wave device*. Since it can work in both directions, there's a wave input and a wave output. The wave input takes sound from a microphone, or some other analog audio source, and digitizes it. The wave output takes digital audio and produces an analog audio signal from it, suitable for sending to a speaker or a radio transmitter.

THE MIXERS

A sound-card mixer is similar in concept to a mixing board you might find in a recording studio or radio station. The simplest kind of audio mixer isn't really a mixer at all, but a switch, which can route any one of several inputs to a single output. More commonly, a mixer combines two or more inputs into a single output, by adding, or *summing*, the signals together. With a set of potentiometers, the audio engineer can adjust the levels of each of the inputs to produce the desired result in the output.

A typical sound card actually contains *two* mixers. This causes some confusion for many computer users, but a look at **Figure 6.9** shows the reason why. One mixer combines each of the sound card's audio sources into the signal that goes to the speakers. This allows the speakers to be shared between the wave out, the music synthesizer, and even the microphone and line inputs.

The other mixer's job is to combine signals into the *input* of the waveform device, rather than working with the output. This is commonly called the recording mixer, or wave-input mixer. Again, the choices of audio sources include the microphone jack, the line-in jack, the music synthesizer, and sometimes even the wave out.

In the innards of the *Windows* multimedia system, the components of a mixer are called *lines* and *controls*. Lines are sources or destinations of audio (called *source lines* and *destination lines*); controls determine how source lines are routed to destination lines, and in what quantities. The idea is that any mixing device, no matter how complex, can be represented by stringing combinations of lines and controls together, in TinkerToy fashion. This way, manufacturers of sophisticated sound cards with dozens of inputs and outputs and all kinds of special effects can simply write drivers for their products, and they can be "dropped in" to work with nearly any existing *Windows* multimedia program.

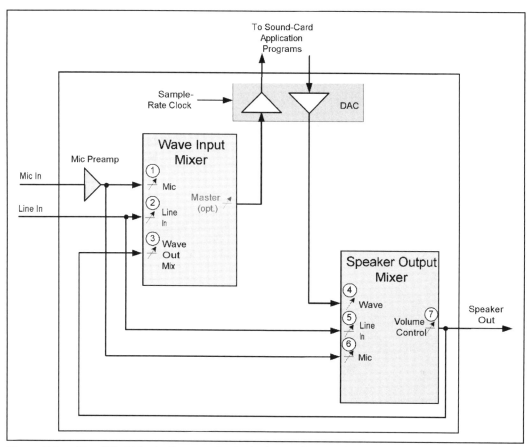

Figure 6.9 — Simplified block diagram of a typical sound card. (Only the waveform audio paths are shown.) The numbered volume controls correspond to the sliders shown in Figures 6.10 and 6.11.

GRAPHICAL MIXER DISPLAYS

An example of a program that works with these drivers is the volume-control applet found in the *Windows XP* Control Panel, usually called Sounds (or Sounds and Multimedia). It's also available by double-clicking the yellow loudspeaker icon in the *Windows* system tray (**Figure 6.10**).

On start-up, the volume-control applet reads the electronic block diagram of the sound card's mixer(s), and displays each control as an appropriate clickable picture, such as a slider or a checkbox. The Playback controls normally come up first, but you can switch to another set of controls, such as the recording controls (**Figure 6.11**), by making a selection from the Properties menu. Typically, the Playback controls correspond to the Speaker Out destination line, and the Recording controls correspond to the Wave Input destination line.

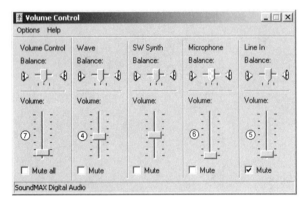

Figure 6.10 — A typical *Windows XP* playback volume control panel. The numbered sliders correspond to the numbers in Figure 6.9. The appearance of this panel varies from one computer to another, depending on the particular sound card's capabilities. Also, not all of the available sliders are necessarily shown. On this particular computer, CD Player and Aux level controls were also available, but were not displayed because they had not been checked under Options-->Properties.

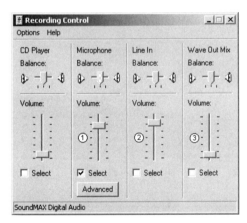

Figure 6.11 — A typical *Windows XP* recording volume control panel. The numbered sliders correspond to the numbers in Figure 6.9. To display this panel, open the Playback volume controls, then choose Recording from the Options -->Properties window. Just as with the playback controls, the type and number of sliders can vary. In this example, the Advanced button appears under the Microphone slider because the sound card has a "mic boost" option, *and* Advanced Controls was checked on the Options menu. Note also the Select check boxes. Although these are shown as check boxes rather than radio buttons, only one input can be selected at a time; some sound cards allow more than one to be selected.

Why does this have to be so complicated? Why not just show three or four sliders, for microphone level, line-in level, and wave out level, for example? This question is often asked by hams who are working with sound-card software for the first time. It's a fair question, but there are at least two reasons why it's done this way. The first is flexibility — some sound cards, for example, have no wave input at all; others have no wave output; others have no microphone line. Still others have a microphone line, but its level is fixed, not adjustable. The second reason is probably due to the way the sound card is typically used. Unlike hams, I suspect that most *Windows* users are only interested in adjusting the levels going to the speakers — "turning the volume up and down." I'd guess that most *Windows* users have never plugged a microphone into their computer, and have no need to adjust the recording levels. So displaying recording level controls automatically might cause unnecessary confusion.

Incidentally, there's an undocumented shortcut for bringing up the Recording controls (instead of the Playback controls) directly. The volume-control applet is called SNDVOL32.EXE, and can be found in the *Windows* directory. If you're running *Windows* versions prior to *Vista* (such as *Windows XP*), you can go straight to the recording controls by typing

```
sndvol32 -r
```

at a command prompt, or creating a desktop shortcut to this command. This will display the Recording controls, as shown in Fig 6.11.

THE AUDIO MIXER ON WINDOWS VISTA

The sound architecture is somewhat different on *Windows Vista*. Not only are the innards of the audio chain somewhat different from *Windows XP*, the graphical controls have changed, too. If you double-click on the speaker icon on a *Vista* machine and choose Mixer, you'll see an applet that looks like **Figure 6.12**. The big change here from *Windows XP* is that each running application that's using the sound card gets its own playback volume slider; note the *EchoLink* control in the rightmost column. When the application closes, its volume slider vanishes, but *Windows* remembers the most recent setting and restores it when the application is restarted.

On *Vista,* the remaining audio controls are reachable from the Windows Control Panel, via the Sound icon. Separate groups of settings control playback and recording. An example of the Recording settings is shown in **Figure 6.13**. If your sound card has several different inputs to choose from (such as Microphone and Line In), *Vista* lists each separately, as if each were a separate device entirely; in this example, you'll notice that the Creative SB Audigy card is listed four times, one for each of its inputs. On the Recording Devices panel, the one that appears with a green check mark is the *preferred* device, which is the one used by any program that doesn't give you a choice. On programs such as *EchoLink* that do offer a choice, you'll see separate choices for Microphone and Line inputs in the list of input devices.

If you installed more than one sound card in other versions of *Windows* and used a program that let you choose which one to

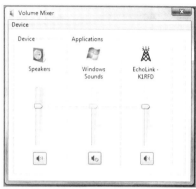

Figure 6.12 — The Mixer applet on *Windows Vista*. The master control and the Windows Sounds slider occupy the first two positions; other applications that are currently using the sound card are listed next, each with its own control.

Figure 6.13 — The Recording tab of the *Vista* sound applet.

Figure 6.14 — Playback level controls for a *Vista* sound device.

use, you'd see the name of each sound card listed. With *Vista*, the list is a bit different, showing the name of each *line* rather than the name of the device.

Playback levels are available by choosing the Playback tab and then clicking Levels (**Figure 6.14**). Here, the picture is more familiar; each of the sliders controls the level of a source that can be mixed into the playback channel (in this case Speakers).

TRANSMIT-RECEIVE SWITCHING

The Internet, and most computer sound cards, work just fine in *full-duplex* mode — they can transmit and receive at the same time. Conventional radio transceivers, however, are not — they are inherently *half-duplex* devices; when they start transmitting, they stop receiving, and vice versa. In one sense, even a conventional 2-meter FM repeater isn't really a full-duplex device. Even though it transmits on one frequency while receiving on another, it can't process signals in both directions simultaneously, and stations using the repeater must take turns to transmit. Unlike telephone conversations, very few Amateur Radio QSOs are full duplex.

What this means is that there must be a mechanism at each end of the Internet link to key the link radio on and off at the appropriate times. The link radio must only transmit when the station at the distant end of the Internet link has something to say, and then switch back to receive mode when the transmission is complete.

The two approaches commonly used for transmit-receiving switching are *carrier detect* (CD) and *voice-operated switch* (VOX).

CD is sometimes also called *carrier-operated switch* (COS) or *carrier-operated relay* (COR), because of its widespread use in FM repeaters to turn the repeater's transmitter on and off automatically. Typically, the receiver's squelch circuit is fitted with a special DC output which swings "high" only when the squelch is open (i.e., while a carrier is being received), and remains "low" at all other times. This allows external equipment, such as a repeater controller or a VoIP system, to detect the presence of a received signal.

VOX is familiar to anyone who has operated an SSB transceiver. When the operator begins speaking into the microphone, the rig starts transmitting. A second after the operator stops speaking, the rig stops transmitting. This is accomplished by a circuit that measures the peak voltage of the audio signal, compares it to a *threshold* voltage, and keys the transmitter if the peak exceeds the threshold. It also resets a timer that keeps the rig keyed for a second or two, to avoid switching between words. In much the same way, VOX can be used at the receiving end as a way of detecting a signal. Since it can be driven by the final audio stage of the receiver, it can be equally useful for FM as for SSB — as long as there's always some audio coming through. Unless it carries a CTCSS tone or background noise, a dead-carrier FM signal won't trigger an audio-based VOX.

Chapter 7

Under the Hood: *EchoLink*

SOFTWARE ARCHITECTURE

EchoLink is designed to be easy to install, configure, and use, yet versatile enough to meet the needs of many different types of nodes. Although fairly simple on the outside, there's a lot happening on the inside during every QSO.

The main components of the *EchoLink* software are shown in **Figure 7.1**. The program operates in either of two modes – *single-user mode* or *sysop mode*. The basic VoIP functions of both modes are the same, but sysop mode adds features to support

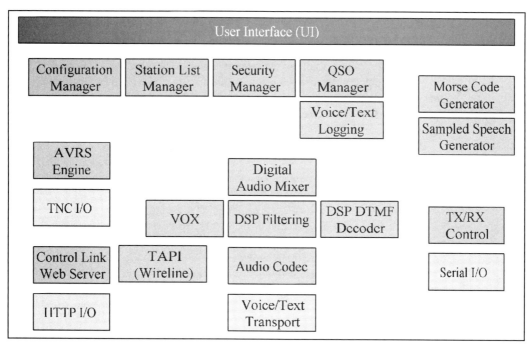

Figure 7.1 — The major internal components of the *EchoLink* software.

a link transceiver or repeater connected to the PC.

Many of the components are familiar from our discussion of digital audio fundamentals. One of its key components is a digital audio mixer, which is used to combine audio signals from several sources (audio codec, Morse generator, and speech generator) before sending them to the computer's sound card. *EchoLink* also includes several built-in digital signal-processing (DSP) functions, including a software-based DTMF decoder, which detects and decodes DTMF commands from the link transceiver.

EchoLink has several different input-output (I/O) functions. Of course, the program exchanges digitized voice data with the computer's sound card. But it also includes a user interface, which accepts commands from the keyboard and mouse and displays the program's status graphically. The program exchanges data with the PC's serial port to control the link equipment, and communicates with the Internet to exchange voice and text data with other stations and authentication and status information with the *EchoLink* servers. In sysop mode, a built-in Web server supports remote management of the node, and a program option sends status information to a TNC for distribution over the local APRS packet network.

One of the questions often asked about *EchoLink* is how the voice announcements are generated in sysop mode. Rather than being synthesized by a text-to-speech generator, the program actually contains short recordings (samples) of an actual voice (my own), and assembles them as needed to create announcements. There are about 50 samples built into the program, including the digits 0 through 9, the letters A through Z, and a short list of words and phrases.

SERVER ARCHITECTURE

EchoLink stations communicate directly with each other over the Internet. This kind of communication is called *peer-to-peer* because there is no master – all stations are on equal footing with each other. System engineers are fond of saying that this arrangement *scales* well, because it allows thousands and thousands of QSOs to take place simultaneously, without creating a bottleneck at some central server.

If each *EchoLink* station kept its own list of every other *EchoLink* station it wanted to communicate with, along with a password (or some other form of authentication), no such central server would be required. However, there are many thousands of registered *EchoLink* stations, with more than 170 new ones coming online every day. Most of these stations use Internet providers that assign *dynamic addresses*, which means their Internet addresses change from time to time. Moreover, it's useful for each station to be able to keep running tabs as to who's online at a given moment, rather than simply keeping a big phone book around.

To meet all of these needs, the *EchoLink* system provides certain services to help get the QSO started. These services are as follows:

• **Authentication**: Finding out who the user is – or making sure he is who he says he is.

• **Access control**: Determining whether the user is allowed to access the system.

• **Discovery**: Finding out who else is logged in to the system, to develop a list of active stations, and to keep track of each station's status.

• **Location**: Keeping track of the Internet address of each station.

EchoLink uses a set of centralized servers, called *addressing servers*, to handle all four of these tasks (**Figure 7.2**). The addressing servers run silently behind the scenes 24 hours a day, and keep track of each station registered with *EchoLink*, which stations are currently logged in, and the Internet address (also called the *IP address*) of each station.

Why does this require more than one server? There are two good reasons: fault tolerance and scalability. The servers are arranged so that each one handles a share of the load – a technique known as *load balancing*. This arrangement also ensures that if one of the servers should fail, the others automatically pick up the slack by taking on an extra share of the load. In fact, two or three of the servers could be down, and the system would still work. Computers (and the Internet) being what they are, this is a welcome feature indeed.

Accomplishing this, however, requires some trickery. There are two sticky problems that must be solved: First, how is it that some *EchoLink* stations can contact one addressing server, and other stations contact another? And second, how can we ensure that no matter which addressing server they contact, each station can "see" the same information at the same time?

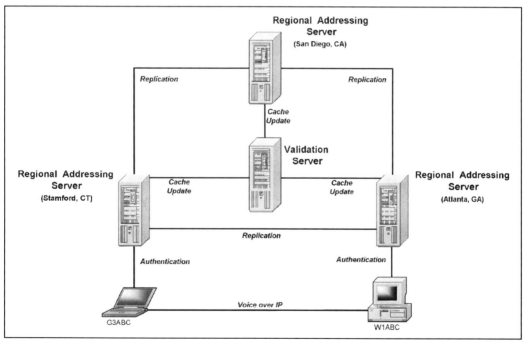

Figure 7.2 — A simplified view of the *EchoLink* server architecture. Three addressing servers are shown. Note that the voice traffic between G3ABC and W1ABC (in this example) travels directly from station to station, and not through the servers.

DNS TO THE RESCUE!

Although there are several ways to balance load across several servers, one of the easiest ways is to take advantage of the Domain Name System, or DNS. DNS is the master telephone book of the Internet, the thing that translates an easy-to-remember name – like www.arrl.org – into a machine-friendly address – like 216.167.96.124. One of the useful features of DNS is its ability to associate more than one IP address with a single name, a little bit like having several different phone numbers in the same household. This type of DNS listing can be set up so that every time the *EchoLink* software requests the IP address of an addressing server, the DNS server spits back a different answer. This mechanism, known as *round-robin load balancing*, is an easy way to send an equal number of requests to any of several different servers, no matter where in the world they are located.

Another useful feature of DNS is just the opposite – the ability to associate more than one name with a single address. These additional names, sometimes called *aliases*, make it possible for a single server to assume multiple identities.

How does this benefit *EchoLink*? When the software is installed, *EchoLink* examines the prefix of your call sign to determine in which country you're likely to be located, by consulting the official ITU prefix list. Based on the name of the country (and, in some cases, the numbered call area within the country), the software assembles a list of the addressing servers most likely to be closest to you geographically. These names are **naeast.echolink.org** for the Eastern part of North America, **nawest.echolink.org** for the Western part, **asia.echolink.org** for Asia, and so forth. The last item in the list is always the generic name **servers.echolink.org**.

This is where DNS steps in. Each of these names is actually an alias rather than a true server name. And although there are six or seven such aliases, there are typically only three or four addressing servers active, so many of these names "point" to the same physical server. Finally, the generic name **servers.echolink.org** has all four physical server addresses associated with it, in the round-robin fashion described above.

What makes this technique attractive is that the *EchoLink* system administrators can adjust the load on each of the addressing servers, to some extent, by changing the way the DNS aliases are assigned. Another nice feature is that the *EchoLink* software will always find a "live" server, regardless of how the list of servers had been assembled. All servers are listed under **servers.echolink.org**, and the *EchoLink* software is designed to work its way through each IP address in the list until it succeeds. Thanks to this design, the *EchoLink* system has remained up and running despite all sorts of hardware, software, and Internet catastrophes (which, fortunately, are now rare).

REPLICATION

The second problem is a little thornier. If W1XYZ is logged in to Server 1, and W6XYZ is logged in to Server 2, how will W1XYZ and W6XYZ ever find out about each other, so they can have a QSO? Clearly, there needs to be some way for the two servers to "talk" to each other so that they know about each other's log-ins. This sort of electronic chatter is called *replication*. Every 20 seconds, each of the addressing servers asks each of the other servers, "Pardon me, but who has logged in (or logged off) since the last time I asked?" (Large, expensive computers are exceptionally polite.) The other server responds with a list of all the changes since the last time that question was asked (i.e., in the past 20 seconds), and so Server 1 has an exact snapshot of what's happening on Server 2.

By asking only for the differences, not the whole list, the conversation takes up a minimal amount of bandwidth. This is an important design feature when you consider how often these exchanges must take place. If four addressing servers are active, each server is asking each of the other three servers for updates every 20 seconds – an average of one question every seven seconds.

Wouldn't it be more efficient to just broadcast a message to all servers each time a station logs in or logs off? Not when you consider how many transactions the addressing servers are handling. As a group, the servers process about one million transactions every 24 hours, an average of 11 transactions per second. By exchanging this information in 20-second batches, each set of changes can be sent in a single, compact package.

AUTHENTICATION AND VALIDATION

The final piece of the puzzle is security, which is an important factor in any Internet-based application. Certainly, Amateur Radio is not particularly secure – no one asks for proof of license or a password when you turn on your rig – but there is heightened sensitivity to security on the Internet because personal computers are in the hands of so many millions of users worldwide, only a small fraction of whom are licensed Amateur Radio operators.

Some of the important aspects of Internet security are authentication, access control, data integrity, and privacy. We've defined authentication and access control already. Data integrity deals with making sure the message hasn't been tampered with since the original sender sent it; privacy deals with making sure no one else can eavesdrop on the conversation.

EchoLink's security model focuses on authentication and access control. The first step is *validation*, which is the process of registering a brand-new user who has just installed the software. The main purpose of validation is to ensure that each user of *EchoLink* is a duly licensed Amateur Radio operator, and if so, to associate a password with his call sign. This process is described in detail in the next section.

Once validated, the user's call sign and password are stored in a database on a special server called the *validation server*. Slimmed-down copies of this database are also kept on each of the addressing servers. Each *EchoLink* user's software must provide his call sign and the matching password to the addressing server before being allowed access. Only after the addressing server has verified the password will the user be logged in, and only after logging in will the *EchoLink* software allow connections to be made to other stations. Furthermore, the *EchoLink* software at the other end will only *accept* connections from stations that are duly logged in, as verified by the addressing server. This two-way security mechanism is particularly efficient since it doesn't require any information to be stored at each *EchoLink* user's computer, except the user's own call sign and password. In effect, each *EchoLink* user's software is delegating authentication to the central server, rather than having to manage it on its own. This kind of *trust-based* authentication is common in many computer systems, particularly those on corporate networks.

However, the *EchoLink* software does allow individual users to make their own access-control rules, over and above basic authentication. You can say, for example, that only stations from Côte D'Ivoire and Finland are allowed to access your link. You can build a list of specific call signs that are to be denied access, or you can limit access to a short list of call signs that are allowed during a special net session. In this way, individual users can make their own rules about access control, while still delegating authentication to the servers.

What about privacy? Certainly, many transactions on the Internet need to be private, and the messages sent back and forth are encrypted. When you use your credit card to buy books, or connect to your company's extranet to learn about the bonus plan, you want some assurance that no one else could be eavesdropping on the conversation. Such is not the case with Amateur Radio, however. Conversations on the air are never private (in fact, FCC rules prohibit using codes or encryption to obscure the meaning of a transmission), so there really isn't a compelling need to ensure the privacy of Internet-linked Amateur Radio communication. Although VoIP data *could* be encrypted, the systems described in this book do not do so, thus saving computer CPU cycles for other tasks.

VALIDATING NEW USERS

None of these security mechanisms is very helpful if there isn't a reliable way to screen new users, to be sure they are indeed licensed Amateurs, and using the call sign that's been assigned to them.

This is where authentication steps in once again. Recall that authentication is the process of ensuring that "you are who you say you are." FCC records might be very clear that WJ2MS is a person named Joseph M. Schmo who lives in Schmoville, NJ, and is an Extra Class licensee whose ticket expires in 2011. But when someone says "I'm WJ2MS; please validate me for *EchoLink*," how do we know it's the real Joe Schmo, and not his evil twin?

Clearly, we need to have something akin to showing a driver's license when you cash a check. If you walk into a supermarket for the first time and whip out your checkbook in the Express lane, the cashier will probably ask you to authenticate yourself by asking for some form of ID. If it's a store you visit every week, you can probably get a check-cashing card, which is a form of ID issued by the supermarket itself, and thus minimize the grumbling of all the people in line behind you.

As you have probably guessed, a good way to prove your identity as a ham is to produce a copy of your amateur license. This is exactly how *EchoLink* validation works. Every new user of the system must provide proof of license and identity, and one option is to scan and upload (or fax) a copy of your ticket. At the other end, one of the *EchoLink* system administrators will review the information, and mark your call sign "validated" if everything checks out. From this point on, the password that you originally chose when you installed the software becomes your key to identify yourself each time you log in.

US hams, with licenses issued by the Federal Communications Commission (FCC), have a couple of other options. If scanning or faxing a license copy is inconvenient, you can choose either the Credit Card or Telephone methods of validation.

The Credit Card method checks your identity by verifying that your credit card's billing address is an exact match for the address you have on file with the FCC for your call sign. When you enter your card number on a secure page on the *EchoLink* Web site, the system does an address verification system (AVS) check and tries to match up your card's address with the data in the FCC database. If it's a match, you're good to go. The only catch here is that some card-issuing banks don't support AVS, so not all cards will work. Also, many hams use a different address on their FCC license than they do for other correspondence, such as a post-office box; if that's the case, there is no way to match up the two addresses.

The Telephone method is an interesting choice if your home telephone number is listed in the phone book (**Figure 7.3**). Visit the *EchoLink* Web site and choose the Telephone method of validation. You'll be provided with a special, unique access code,

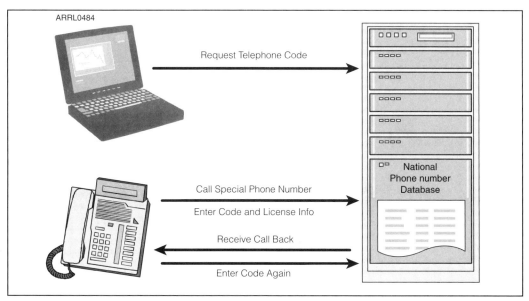

ARRL0484

Request Telephone Code

Call Special Phone Number

Enter Code and License Info

Receive Call Back

Enter Code Again

National Phone number Database

Figure 7.3 — *EchoLink*'s **telephone validation system. The automated system verifies the caller's identity by comparing the information in the national telephone directory with the information in the FCC database.**

and a telephone number to call. Place the call from your regular home telephone (not a cell phone), enter the access code, and answer a couple of other questions using the DTMF pad on your phone. When prompted, hang up and wait for a call back from the *EchoLink* system a few seconds later. When you answer, you'll be asked for the access code once again, and then you're validated. What happens behind the scenes is that the *EchoLink* system has done a reverse-lookup check of your phone number in the electronic national directory, to get the corresponding name and address. It compares this with the name and address in the FCC database for the call sign you're trying to validate. If there's a match, and the call back to your phone was successful, the verification is done. For Telephone validation, the important thing is that your phone listing matches the FCC mailing address, and that your phone number is fully published. Keep in mind that some local phone companies don't publish this information nationally, or publish only a name and not a street address. But the nice things about this system are that it's fast and it's fully automated.

The *EchoLink* administrators, who work around the clock in several different time zones, also have at their disposal specially-designed tools for managing the user database, incoming e-mail, tracking logs, and international call sign databases, all as part of the validation process. A number of countries, such as the United States, Canada, Brazil, Japan, and France offer downloadable or searchable databases of Amateur Radio license records. The *EchoLink* back-end system maintains local *mirrors* (copies) of some of these databases to further cross-check validation requests, such as ensuring that the requestor's license has not already expired or been cancelled. (You might be surprised to learn that more than half of the *EchoLink* software suite, in terms of lines of code, lies in the authentication and validation systems that users never actually see!)

But today *EchoLink*, and tomorrow perhaps *MegaLink*, and *DXLink*, and *5By9Link*. As more and more Internet-based Amateur Radio applications emerge, will each one require its users (and administrators) to go through the same gyrations, in order to ensure security?

Fortunately, the answer is "no." Just as the check-cashing card is to the supermarket chain, the *digital certificate* is to the Amateur Radio Service. The idea is that a ham should only have to authenticate herself once to some trusted organization, and from then on, just present her digital ID card to anyone else who needs it.

In September 2003, the ARRL inaugurated its *Logbook of the World* (LoTW) program. LoTW is an Internet-based system for submitting entries from your logbook, in order to verify QSOs and qualify for awards such as WAS and DXCC. Like an electronic QSL card, an entry is considered valid if both you and the other station have reported the same QSO to LoTW.

Critical to the success of LoTW is strong authentication. If you want to participate in LoTW, you request a digital certificate from the ARRL. The ARRL staff then authenticates you, either by asking you for copies of documentation, or by sending a postcard with a special code to your registered mailing address. Once you're authenticated, you receive a signed digital certificate (by e-mail), and you're ready to submit log entries to LoTW.

Like an ATM card, you can't use a digital certificate to prove your identity unless you know the secret *private key*, or at least have access to it. This is analogous to the PIN for your ATM card. Usually, your private key is stored on your computer, and kept locked up with a password. The matching *public key* is stored in the digital certificate itself, which you can freely give out to anyone who needs to authenticate you.

To prove your identity, you "sign" a message with your private key, and then send the message, the electronic signature, and the digital certificate to the person who needs it. That person then verifies the signature by using the public key to decrypt it, and checking to be sure the signature matches the message, and that the certificate is valid. If everything checks out, he can be sure it was you who sent it.

This sounds like quite a long process, but it can all be done in a fraction of a second by computers at both ends of the conversation. In fact, it's exactly what happens when you visit a secure Web site with your Web browser, except that the roles are reversed – the Web site is authenticating itself to you.

The best part is that once you have this digital certificate, you can use it as an electronic ID card for other Amateur Radio systems that are set up to accept it. Among those that do is *EchoLink*. As an alternative to submitting a photocopy of your license, *EchoLink* provides a special utility that will generate a validation request, sign it, and send it (along with your digital certificate) to the *EchoLink* servers. If the signature is verified at the other end, you've been authenticated successfully. Quite a bit easier than sending a copy of your license!

At the heart of this arrangement is *trust*. In effect, *EchoLink* trusts the ARRL to properly verify the identity of each user to whom it provides a digital certificate. The certificate itself is signed by the ARRL, which in this scenario is acting as the *certification authority* (CA). Currently, the ARRL is the only CA that *EchoLink* recognizes, but there may be other organizations added to this list in the future. In this example, *EchoLink* is not a CA, just another party in the transaction.

LOGGING IN

Once a call sign has been validated for use with *EchoLink*, its password is stored alongside the call sign in the master *user database*, and distributed to the cached database at each regional addressing server. When the new user starts up the *EchoLink* software a second time, the software "logs in" to one of the addressing servers by providing this call sign and password.

However, to avoid sending the password "in the clear" over the Internet, the password is encrypted. Enter public-key cryptography once again! Each addressing server has a public key. On start-up, the *EchoLink* software requests the server's public key and a challenge phrase – a random, unique string of characters concocted each time by the server. Using the server's public key, the *EchoLink* software then encrypts both the password and the challenge phrase, and sends this encrypted message to the server. The server decrypts the message with its private key, and then verifies that both the challenge phrase and the password are correct. If so, the user's call sign is marked as "logged in," and his node can begin connecting to other stations in the *EchoLink* system.

VOX CONTROL

EchoLink has an optional, built-in VOX (an acronym for "voice operated switch") that can be used in Sysop mode to detect a signal on the receiver. Although it's implemented in software rather than hardware, it functions very much like the VOX circuit in an SSB transceiver. When the peak (sampled) voltage of the audio input reaches a certain threshold, the VOX is triggered and engaged, and a timer is started. When the timer expires, the VOX is released.

VOX might seem like a poor choice for detecting the presence of FM signals, but it can give reasonably good results in situations where a more positive, direct method of carrier detect is unavailable or impractical. For example, it's commonly used when the link receiver is tuned to the output frequency of a repeater. Most repeaters have a "tail" of 5 or 10 seconds during which the carrier remains on after the last transmission ceases. In this situation, a VOX can distinguish between a voice signal and a dead carrier, whereas a direct carrier-detect circuit cannot.

However, there are several problems with this technique. One problem is that if the VOX is adjusted to ignore a dead carrier, it might also drop out during a pause between sentences, giving a remote station the impression that it's now his turn to transmit.

A second problem is that other audio signals, such as squelch tails and noise bursts, will also trigger the VOX. This is clearly undesirable for an Internet link, which is inherently half-duplex. For example, even if the "anti-thump" or "pulseback" timer is adjusted so that the link receiver ignores its own squelch tail, the *repeater's* squelch tail is heard 5 to 10 seconds later. Ideally, a VOX could be made "smart" so that it ignored these non-voice signals.

EchoLink has just such a feature. It can be enabled in Sysop mode by engaging an option called Squelch Crash Anti-Trip (SCAT). Using digital signal processing techniques and a digital delay line, when properly adjusted, it will cause *EchoLink*'s VOX to ignore short bursts of noise.

Figure 7.4 shows the audio envelope of the end of a typical transmission from a repeater, as seen by a link receiver tuned to the repeater's output. Note that the courtesy tone and the squelch tail each have a characteristic signature: a short burst of noise surrounded on both sides by silence.

Figure 7.5 shows how the Smart VOX works. After sampling and digitizing the incoming audio, it is placed into a queue — a digital delay line. A representation of the signal's envelope is obtained by passing the signal through a digital low-pass filter. The program examines the envelope, compares the peak amplitude to the VOX threshold, and checks the amplitude of the signal immediately before and after it in time. The VOX is triggered only if the signal doesn't match the characteristics of a noise burst. At the end of the delay line, the audio is passed through to the Internet transport. The delay line ensures that no part of the signal is clipped by the VOX due to its delayed triggering.

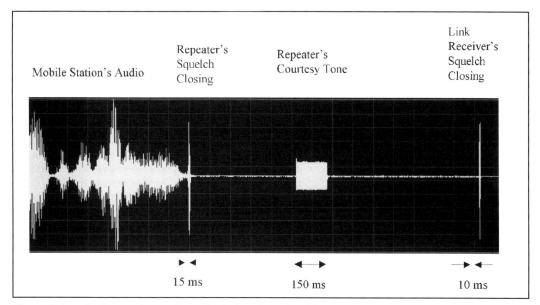

Figure 7.4 — Audio envelope of a typical signal received from an FM repeater.

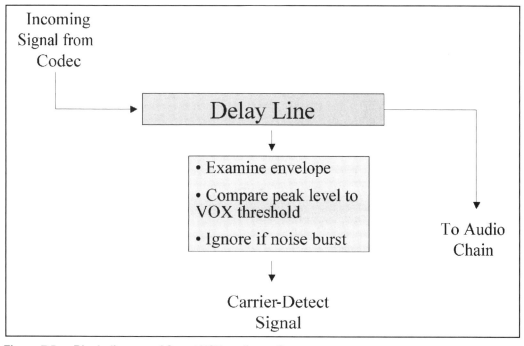

Figure 7.5 — Block diagram of Smart VOX audio routing.

POSITIVE CARRIER DETECT

VOX is convenient, but it has its shortcomings. One problem is that when the Smart VOX feature is enabled, it introduces an extra delay in the audio path. Each additional delay makes a QSO less like a natural conversation, and makes it more difficult for other stations to break in. And even with Smart VOX in force, *EchoLink* still won't be able to track incoming signals perfectly.

A much better solution is to spend some time finding a way to use *positive carrier detect* to detect incoming signals, especially if your node is serving a local repeater rather than a simplex frequency. The goal here is to provide a way for *EchoLink* to track the exact beginning and end of each transmission as seen from the repeater's input, rather than its output. There are several ways to do this, depending on how the repeater is set up, and whether the Internet linking equipment is located at the repeater site, or at a remote location.

COS from Repeater Receiver: If the node is hard-wired to the repeater controller, the best source of carrier detect is the COS output from the repeater receiver itself — or an equivalent signal from the repeater controller. This ensures that the node transmits to the Internet only when a signal is being received on the input. Also, the audio connection to the sound card should come from the receiver's audio output, rather than the repeater transmitter's audio path. Most modern-day repeater controllers provide one or more additional ports for connecting auxiliary receivers and transmitters; this is often a good place to make a direct connection to the Internet link. You may still need a simple interface to present the proper signals to the computer, however.

COS from Link Transceiver: If the node is remotely located, it may be desirable to use the COS signal from the link transceiver — but only if the repeater's "tail" is extremely short. Otherwise, the node will keep transmitting to the Internet 5 to 10 seconds after the local user finishes a transmission, severely interrupting the flow of a QSO. Some repeater-node operators have successfully incorporated DTMF tones in their custom Connect and Disconnect announcements to automatically shorten the repeater's "tail" while a station is connected, on repeaters that support this type of remote command.

CTCSS Control: If the node is remotely located, this may be the best technique of all — but it requires cooperation from the repeater. In this set-up, the repeater transmits a CTCSS (a.k.a. PL) tone only while its receiver's COS is active; that is, only while a station is transmitting. The *EchoLink* transceiver is configured to open up only when this tone is received. The advantage of this system is that *EchoLink* triggers only on a true signal, and ignores incidentals such as courtesy tones and CW IDs. The disadvantage is that most PL-guarded repeaters transmit a continuous tone, even when no signal is present on the input, so it may require configuration changes to the repeater itself. (Note that this technique can be used whether or a not a PL is required to activate the repeater.)

REMOTE CONTROL

Fortunately, many countries (with some notable exceptions) currently do not require that stations running as Internet voice gateways have a control operator sitting in front of the radio. Instead, the rules allow link stations to be operated under either *automatic control* or *remote control*. (For a more complete discussion, see the chapter "Legal Issues.")

There are two ways to perform remote control of a link station: over an RF link, or over a wireline link. *EchoLink* has built-in features to support three types of control links:

• **RF control**. Linking interfaces (and multi-purpose interfaces) for *EchoLink* usually have a second audio input, for connecting a control receiver (such as a UHF receiver). The audio from the control receiver is routed into the DTMF decoder on the board, but not into the audio path that feeds the computer's sound card. This allows a control operator to send DTMF commands over a control link frequency without the commands being heard over the air.

• **Internet control**. *EchoLink* has a simple, built-in Web server that hosts a single, master control page. When properly configured, the control link can be accessed from any Internet Web browser in the world, given the right security credentials. From this page, the control operator can enable or disable the link, connect or disconnect a station, and view the recent status log.

• **Dial-in control**. If the PC is equipped with a *voice modem*, such as the type used for PC-based telephone answering machines, *EchoLink* has an option that allows a control operator to dial in from a touch-tone telephone and enter DTMF commands to control the link, without the commands being heard over the air. This feature is similar to the telephone-line control available on some repeater controllers. The control op can also hear the transmitted or received audio over the dial-in connection.

Even though radio regulations may require that a wireline or RF control link be in place when an Internet voice gateway is operating, it doesn't necessarily imply that *all* control functions must be performed over this link. More often, it is used as a backup in case the primary input frequency of the link is busy or otherwise unreachable. For example, you might normally disconnect the link by sending a DTMF pound sign (#) over the gateway's input frequency, but you would have to use the wireline or RF control link to disconnect the link if it's connected to a long-winded roundtable QSO and none of the stations is leaving a long enough pause to let the VOX drop.

Remote control of an Internet link is a big subject, and an important one. Chapter 10, "Remote Control Techniques," offers some interesting solutions for either *EchoLink* or *IRLP*.

ROUTERS AND FIREWALLS

Your node's connection to the Internet might be going through a *router* or a *firewall*. These devices can improve the security of your computer, and can allow a single Internet address to be shared by more than one computer on your network.

However, routers and firewalls can be a problem for peer-to-peer networks such as VoIP linking systems. The reason is that nodes communicate directly with each other over the Internet, rather than sending all of their packets through a central server. (eQSO is a notable exception, however.) This is good for the efficiency and scale of the system, but it is not always "firewall-friendly."

By far, the most common problem involves a device called a NAT router. Now that broadband Internet connections are so common, NAT routers are more widespread than ever. NAT stands for *network address translation*. If you have a home network or DSL service, you're likely to have one of these. It poses a problem for linking systems because it normally does not allow unsolicited packets from the Internet to reach your PC. The solution to this problem is to configure the *port-forwarding* feature of the router to allow certain packets to reach the IRLP or EchoLink software.

However, port forwarding is not always a good solution. Each make and model of router has a different procedure for setting up port forwarding, so the steps to follow aren't easy to document. (A good starting point, however, is the Web site portforward. com, which aims to provide detailed instructions for many different types of routers.) Furthermore, in many situations, (such as public Wi-Fi hotspots and wireless Internet service) you might not even have access to the router to be able to change its configuration.

GO WITH THE FLOW

EchoLink has a special feature that allows it to work through most types of NAT routers without any special configuration changes. It accomplishes this by automatically setting up a *flow* within the router when a new connection is being established.

Firewall-friendliness is a feature of version 2.0 or above of the software. Although this is the version of *EchoLink* most commonly found in the system, many nodes are still running earlier versions. Until all nodes on the system upgrade to 2.0, some types of connections still won't work through an unconfigured NAT router.

If you're running 2.0 behind a NAT router, you may find that you can connect to conference servers, *EchoIRLP* nodes, and *EchoLink* nodes running 2.0 or above without making any adjustments to your router. To connect to other nodes, you'll need to adjust your router just as before.

It's still a good idea to configure Port Forwarding in your NAT router for use with *EchoLink*, if you can. The firewall-friendly feature is provided as a convenience for users who are unsure about how to configure their router, or who are using a type of Internet service that doesn't allow router changes, such as a satellite ISP or a public hotspot.

But let's back up a second, here. How is it that a program like *EchoLink* can do an end-run around a router, without having to reach into the router and tell it how to set itself up for port forwarding?

There are two parts to it (**Figure 7.6**). The first is simple; the program now uses the same ports (5198 and 5199) for both source and destination when it sends UDP packets. Prior to this, it used dynamically-assigned source port numbers. Most types of NAT routers will establish a *flow* when they see a request and a corresponding response with precisely reversed addresses (including port number), allowing other unsolicited

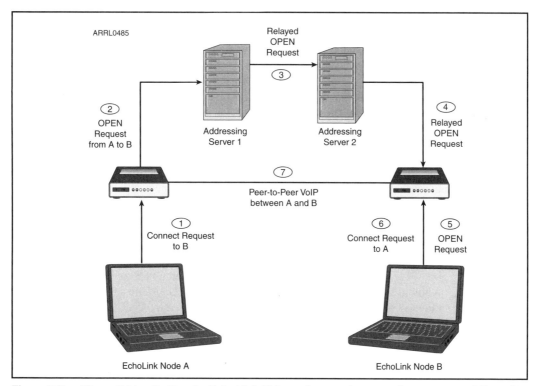

Figure 7.6 — Firewall-friendly flow in *EchoLink*. This system works around most types of firewalls by setting up a *flow* at each end, with the help of the addressing servers.

packets to be received over the same flow within a certain time period. Using fixed source ports ensures that the source and destination addresses are exactly swapped in a response packet. This also avoids false triggering of denial-of-service protections built into some firewalls, which had been a problem for a few users.

The second part is a way to accommodate a firewall on incoming connections. When a node initiates a connection, it sends an additional packet to its addressing server indicating that it wishes to connect to the other node. The addressing server relays this request to the receiving node, which responds by sending a pair of packets back to the initiating node to establish the flow described above. (Nodes maintain a UDP flow with the addressing server to prepare to receive these requests by sending packets to it periodically.) This works even if the two nodes are on different addressing servers, because these connection-request packets are relayed internally amongst the addressing servers as well.

ECHOLINK PROXY

Systems such as *EchoLink* are peer-to-peer system, by designs. This means that when your node is connected to another node over the Internet, the voice and text signals are sent directly from one node to the other, rather than going through some central server. This helps ensure that the system is scalable and reliable.

Unfortunately, there are certain situations in which peer-to-peer connections such as these are difficult to establish. A growing number of Internet providers are offering "one-way" access to the Internet — allowing your computer to initiate a connection, but not to accept one. These include wireless community networks, or hotspots. An example is the wireless Internet service now being provided by many hotels to their guests. Guests with wireless-enabled laptop computers can check their e-mail and surf the Web from their rooms. The hotel uses a router with a fast Internet connection and a single public address (or a small pool of addresses) shared amongst all guests. This arrangement does not work with *EchoLink*, because the guests' computers are not reachable from the Internet. It's the same NAT issue just discussed.

THE PROXY SOLUTION

A solution to this problem is to split the *EchoLink* software into two pieces — one that runs on your laptop, and the other that runs on a PC in some other location with good Internet access. With this arrangement, the laptop need only establish a single, outbound Internet connection to the PC. Then, the *EchoLink* software on the laptop "tunnels" all traffic through this connection to the remote PC, and the PC in turn establishes all of the necessary peer-to-peer connections to other *EchoLink* nodes. In this scenario, the PC is acting as a proxy on behalf of the laptop.

EchoLink offers special software to make this possible. The proxy software, which is designed specifically for use with *EchoLink*, is called *EchoLink* Proxy. **Figure 7.7** illustrates how *EchoLink* Proxy can be used.

IS ECHOLINK PROXY FOR YOU?

Consider setting up *EchoLink* Proxy only if *both* of the following are true:
• You have a fast, true, dedicated Internet connection at your home or office, or at some other place to which you have access to a PC, *and*
• You have "one-way" Internet service at some other location, or you often travel to such a place, such as an airport lounge, coffee shop, or hotel room.

Note that *EchoLink* Proxy will not help if you are simply having trouble connecting to other stations from your home PC. In fact, you must first ensure that EchoLink works correctly on the machine on which the proxy will be installed.

Also, note that a given *EchoLink* Proxy can be used by only one *EchoLink* client machine at a time, since each logged-in *EchoLink* node (or its proxy) must still have a unique public IP address. You can run more than one instance of *EchoLink* Proxy on a PC only if the PC has multiple public Internet addresses, which is uncommon.

Finally, the proxy PC must be reachable through a static public Internet address, or a dynamic public address that can easily be determined remotely.

PUBLIC PROXIES

It's not always convenient or possible to set up an *EchoLink* Proxy machine at a second location. Fortunately, it's not always necessary! Some very generous folks

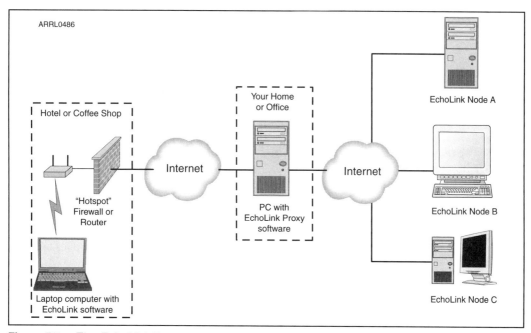

Figure 7.7 — The *EchoLink* Proxy.

have donated their CPU time and bandwidth (not to mention their *own* time) to run instances of the EchoLink Proxy that are available for anyone who wants to use them. This is a tremendously useful resource for the traveling laptop user, who might never know when she'll run into a problem with an unknown firewall.

The list of available *public proxies* appears on the *EchoLink* Web site, updated in real time, but the easiest way to select a public proxy is from the *EchoLink* software itself. Go to the Setup item on the Tools menu, then click the Proxy tab. Click the Public Proxy radio button and pick the name of a proxy from the drop-down list. (The list will only show proxies that are not already busy.) It usually makes no difference which one you choose, as long as it's reachable over the Internet. When you click OK, *EchoLink* re-configures itself automatically to use the proxy you selected, for the remainder of your session.

Do keep in mind that public proxies are a limited, shared resource, so they should be used sparingly. Most proxies do not accept connections from sysop-mode nodes (those with –L or –R suffixes), and some enforce connect-time limits per session.

DISADVANTAGES

There are two key disadvantages to using *EchoLink* Proxy versus the regular *EchoLink* software:

• Voice messages are being transferred between the client and proxy over TCP, rather than UDP. TCP is not designed to handle this type of data, and tends to magnify any problems with congestion along the path.

• Two computers (and Internet connections) are required, rather than just one. It is necessary to run the Proxy software continuously on some remote server, unless you use a public proxy as described above.

SCRIPTING AND AUTOMATION

After using the *EchoLink* software, if you're like most enterprising Amateurs, it won't be long before you'll be thinking of ways it could be improved or extended. Plenty of features and configuration options are included in the program, but it would be impossible (or at least, impractical) to try to cram in every imaginable bell and whistle. Some programs suffer from a malady called "Featureitis" when the whole kitchen sink is thrown in.

Fortunately, *EchoLink* is extendable. Like many *Windows* programs, it includes an *Automation interface*, which is a mechanism by which other programs (or scripts) can interact with it under the covers. Virtually all of the program's functions and options can be controlled this way, and *EchoLink* can also fire *event notifications* when significant things happen, such as another station connecting to yours. This opens up plenty of possibilities for automating or enhancing *EchoLink*.

Automation is part of the component object model (COM) specification championed by Microsoft. In the COM Automation paradigm, clients control servers, and servers can send event notifications to clients. In this context, a "server" is just a program (or a piece of a program) that provides something useful to other programs. You can think of *EchoLink* as a COM server that provides Amateur VoIP linking services to other programs on your computer.

Client programs can be written in any programming language or scripting language that supports COM or .NET. The most popular language for COM clients is probably Visual Basic (including VB.NET). If you've had any experience writing Visual Basic programs, interfacing with *EchoLink* will be a snap, since COM Automation is fully baked into the VB environment. *C++* developers familiar with COM will also find an easy fit (in fact, *EchoLink* itself was developed in the *C++* programming language). COM components can also be accessed from any language supported by the .NET environment, such as *C#*.

Another option is to write a client program using a scripting language. The VB-Script and Jscript languages are built into every *Windows* computer, but it's also possible to write client programs in *Perl* or *Python* after installing the appropriate engine. Scripting languages are a good choice for quick-and-dirty tasks that don't require a user interface, such as starting or stopping *EchoLink*, or commanding it to connect or disconnect according to a schedule.

Several VBScript examples are installed along with the *EchoLink* software, including examples of scripts that receive events from *EchoLink* and respond to them. Complete details of the COM interface, also called the API, are available in the *EchoLink* Programmer's Guide, which can be downloaded from the *EchoLink* Web site.

With some imagination and a modicum of programming skill, you can create programs or scripts that:

• Enable or disable *EchoLink* (in Sysop mode) according to a schedule. Use *Windows* Task Scheduler to run either an "Enable" script or a "Disable" script at pre-set times.

• Connect to specific stations in response to other events. For example, you could create a script that conferences-in W1XYZ each time W2XXX connects.

•Extend the existing set of DTMF commands. Each DTMF string received by *EchoLink*'s decoder fires an Automation event. Your program can receive this event and take appropriate action. This could be used, for example, to control other devices connected to the PC.

•Extend the remote Web control capabilities, in Sysop mode. *EchoLink*'s built-in Web server is very basic, but you can create your own Web interface (using Web server software) that provides many more features and functions.

A few real-world script examples are shown below. The example in **Figure 7.8** is a VBScript script that runs in the *Windows* Scripting Host environment (cscript.exe), and takes advantage of WSH's support for Automation events.

The example in **Figure 7.9** is a short *Perl* program that connects to *EchoLink* using the Win32 OLE module shipped with ActiveState's *ActivePerl*. (It is also possible to use WSH with a *PerlScript* script; see the ActiveState documentation for more information.)

Figure 7.10 is a *C++* version of the *Perl* program in Figure 7.9. It uses the #import technique (supported by Visual Studio) to generate a set of smart-pointer classes from *EchoLink*'s type library.

These are just a few examples as food for thought. If you're a little rusty on COM programming, consult one of the many books on the subject. *Visual Basic 6* (or *Visual Studio .NET*) is probably the easiest development tool with which to get started writing companion programs for *EchoLink*.

LOCAL CONTROL IN SYSOP MODE

Many stations running *EchoLink* as an RF gateway (i.e., with a -L or -R suffix) have the computer located in the shack, or in some other easy-to-reach location. It would seem natural to be able to use the link using a microphone plugged into the PC's sound card, rather than having to pick up an handheld transceiver just to answer a call or join a QSO in progress.

Fortunately, there is a feature in *EchoLink* that allows you to do just that. With the right hardware and software settings, you can use a local microphone alongside the RF gear, and when you transmit, you'll be heard by the remotely-connected station (over the Internet) as well as over your own RF link.

The key is to connect the PC microphone to the *Microphone* jack of your PC's sound card, and connect the audio from the link receiver to the *Line-In* jack. This allows *EchoLink* to switch between the two inputs on the fly.

Here are the other steps:

1. Set your *Windows* Recording Volume controls so that *both* the Line and Microphone inputs are turned up to normal levels. *EchoLink* will use the Mute or Select controls to switch between the two.

2. On your *Windows* Playback Volume control panel, turn up the Microphone slider. This allows audio from the microphone to travel to the audio input of your RF link transmitter. (If you have PC speakers connected, you might need to turn down their volume a bit to avoid feedback.)*EchoLink* will use the Mute control, if available, to switch the microphone on and off.

```
'ConnectWhenReady.vbs: Wait until the specified station comes online, then
connect to it.

'Author: Jonathan Taylor, K1RFD
'Date: July 23, 2003

'To invoke this script from the command line, type:
'        cscript ConnectWhenReady.vbs call sign
'where "call sign" is the call sign of the station to which to connect.
'This script should only be run if EchoLink is already running.


If WScript.Arguments.Count > 0 Then

        sStation = UCase(WScript.Arguments(0))

        'Instantiate EchoLink's Session component, and set up an event
connection
        Set oEchoLink = WScript.CreateObject("EchoLink.EchoLinkSession",
"EchoLink_")

        'get a fresh copy of the station list to kick things off
        'oEchoLink.RefreshStationList True

        'is the desired station already online?
        If IsStationOnlineAndNotBusy(sStation) Then
                oEchoLink.Connect sStation, True
                WScript.Quit(0)
        Else
                'sleep and let events drive things from now on
                WScript.Echo "Sleeping..."
                While True
                        WScript.Sleep 1000
                Wend
        End If
End If

Sub EchoLink_Closing
        'EchoLink is shutting down; exit now to avoid picking daisies
        WScript.DisconnectObject(oEchoLink)
        Set oEchoLink = Nothing
        WScript.Quit(0)
End Sub


Sub EchoLink_StationListReceived

        'This event fires each time the Station List is refreshed.
        'Check the revised station list
        'for the desired call sign; go back to sleep if not found.

        If IsStationOnlineAndNotBusy(sStation) Then
                oEchoLink.Connect sStation, True
                WScript.Quit(0)
        End If
End Sub
```

Figure 7.8 — A *VBScript* example, including event hooks.

```perl
#! .perl

#Connect.pl: Attempt to connect EchoLink to the specified station.

#Author: Jonathan Taylor, K1RFD
#Date: December 3, 2003

#To invoke this script from the command line, type:
#     perl Connect.pl call sign
#where "call sign" is the call sign of the station to which to connect.


use strict;
use Win32::OLE;
my $el = Win32::OLE->new('EchoLink.EchoLinkSession');

#get a fresh copy of the station list; also ensures that
#  EchoLink is fully initialized
$el->RefreshStationList(1);

#attempt the connect
my $station = uc($ARGV[0]);
$el->Connect($station, 1);

#check the results
my $bConnected = $el->IsPeerConnected($station);
if ($bConnected ) {
     print "Connect succeeded.";
} else {
     print "Connect failed.";
}
```

Figure 7.9 — A *Perl* example.

3. In *EchoLink*, under Tools->Sysop Settings, choose the TX Ctrl tab and check the box marked "Key PTT On Local Transmit." This will key the link transmitter whenever you "key" *EchoLink*'s TX, such as by pressing the space bar.

4. Under Tools->Preferences, choose the Connections tab, click "PTT Control," and check the box marked "Auto-Select Mic Input." This will switch the Recording mixer over to Microphone input when you TX locally, instead of taking the link receiver's audio from Line-In.

If you are running in Sysop mode, it's also possible to connect a local push-to-talk switch to your computer's serial port. This would be a natural arrangement if your local microphone is a communications-type mic with a built-in PTT switch. Here are the additional steps:

1. Connect the push-to-talk switch to the COM port connector in such a way that the CTS pin goes high (or low) when you press the button, or vice versa. A typical arrangement is to connect the PTT switch between CTS and ground (pins 8 and 5 on a DB-9 connector) and then pull the CTS pin normally high with a resistor to a 5-12V dc power source. When the switch is pressed, the CTS pin goes low.

2. Under Tools->Preferences, choose the Connections tab, click "PTT Control," and

```cpp
// ELConnect.cpp: Attempt to connect EchoLink to the specified station.

// Author: Jonathan Taylor, K1RFD
// Date: December 3, 2003

#include <windows.h>
#include <stdio.h>

#import "\Program Files\K1RFD\EchoLink\EchoLink.exe" no_namespace

int main(int argc, char* argv[])
{
        CoInitialize(NULL);

        IEchoLinkSessionPtr pEL;
        HRESULT hr = pEL.CreateInstance(__uuidof(EchoLinkSession));
        if (SUCCEEDED(hr)) {

                try {

                        // get a fresh copy of the station list; also ensures that
                        //  EchoLink is fully initialized
                        pEL->RefreshStationList(VARIANT_TRUE);

                        // attempt the connect
                        _bstr_t sStation = argv[1];
                        pEL->Connect(sStation, VARIANT_TRUE);

                        // check the results
                        VARIANT_BOOL bConnected = pEL->IsPeerConnected(sStation);

                        if (bConnected) {
                                printf("Connect succeeded.\n");
                        } else {
                                printf("Connect failed.\n");
                        }
                } catch (_com_error e) {
                        printf("Error: %s\n", (char *)e.Description());
                }


        }

        CoUninitialize();

        return 0;
}
```

Figure 7.10 — A *C++* example.

check the box marked "Serial Port CTS." Then, choose the correct COM port, and check the box marked "Active Low" if the CTS pin goes low on transmit, rather than high.

Verify the configuration by connecting to the Test Server and ensuring that *EchoLink* goes into TX whenever the PTT button is pressed.

LOGGING

EchoLink has several logging features that provide useful historical information about usage of the link.

• **Call sign log**: This is a text file with one line for each QSO, including the date, time, call sign, and description of each station to which your node has connected. The log entry is recorded at the moment the station disconnects. This log is the closest equivalent to a typical Amateur station log file, and is in a format that can be easily imported into spreadsheets or logging programs. A portion of a typical call sign log is shown in **Figure 7.11**.

• **System log**: The System log records all important information about operation

```
2003-12-18 16:55:11 2003-12-18 17:08:00 W1CDM-R    CONF            SAN DIEGO, CA
2003-12-18 18:57:38 2003-12-18 18:59:38 G0MEJ       Nigel P         NW Eng (1)
2003-12-18 20:18:20 2003-12-18 20:19:25 N9TEV       Jeffrey Geiger  Antigo wi 54409
2003-12-18 20:38:30 2003-12-18 20:38:43 VU3GTF      KARAN           NEW DELHI , INDIA (1)
2003-12-18 21:05:10 2003-12-18 21:09:09 KA2LOG-L    CONF            New Rochelle, NY (1)
2003-12-18 21:16:22 2003-12-18 21:17:34 KC2MHA      Tommy           Staten Island, NY
2003-12-18 21:35:36 2003-12-18 21:38:27 N1LRC       Randy           East Bridgewater Ma.
2003-12-18 22:10:36 2003-12-18 22:12:22 KF4OHI-L    Charles         Houston, TX.   USA
2003-12-18 22:14:10 2003-12-18 22:16:23 KF4OHI-L    CONF            Houston, TX.   USA
2003-12-18 22:24:06 2003-12-18 22:25:41 KB2DY       Pete            Massapequa, New York
```

Figure 7.11 — A portion of an *EchoLink* Call sign log file.

```
2003-12-19 08:21:23 Connect WA2TQI-L         BILL 9626 141.150.204.138
2003-12-19 08:22:27 Disconnect WA2TQI-L Peer requested disconnect
2003-12-19 09:33:34 DTMFCommand 01
2003-12-19 09:33:38 Connect LU5ACJ-L         JUAN 27949 24.232.82.61
2003-12-19 09:35:00 DTMFCommand #
2003-12-19 09:35:00 Disconnect LU5ACJ-L DTMF Disconnect command
2003-12-19 10:25:49 Connect IT9GUO          Massimo 155661 151.38.65.153
2003-12-19 10:27:23 Disconnect IT9GUO Peer requested disconnect
2003-12-19 11:49:58 Connect WA1APP          David L. 79444 172.208.53.245
2003-12-19 11:50:24 Disconnect WA1APP Peer requested disconnect
2003-12-19 12:22:12 Verifying WT1I           donald Ridley 68.101.77.115
2003-12-19 12:22:17 Connect WT1I             donald Ridley - 68.101.77.115
2003-12-19 12:24:05 Disconnect WT1I Peer requested disconnect
2003-12-19 13:12:42 Connect KE4BHA           Robert Batten 113452 216.76.211.192
2003-12-19 13:13:33 Disconnect KE4BHA Peer requested disconnect
```

Figure 7.12 — A portion of an *EchoLink* System log file.

of the link, such as stations connecting and disconnecting, DTMF codes received, and start-up and shutdown of the link itself. A portion of a typical System log is shown in **Figure 7.12**.

• **Sound files**: *EchoLink* has an option to "tape record" QSOs that take place over the link, providing the ultimate record of what was said, when it was said, and by whom. When this option is enabled, *EchoLink* stores all incoming and outgoing audio signals as WAV files. These files can be played back at any time in the future using a utility such as *Windows Media Player*. Depending on the settings, *EchoLink* will either record each transmission as a separate file (tagged with the call sign of the sender), or put all transmissions in a single QSO together as a larger file. In either mode, it automatically removes periods of silence, to keep the files small and to make it easier to review them.

ECHOLINK ON WINE

Hardly a week goes by when someone doesn't send an e-mail asking if there is a version of *EchoLink* that runs on *Linux*. Although desktop installations of *Linux* lag far behind the installed base of *Windows* and *Mac OS* machines, the future of *Linux* distributions is bright, and no doubt its rapid acceptance as a server operating system will soon make its way to a big chunk of desktop PCs.

Converting a large, native *Windows* program to run on another operating system (called *porting* the program) is no mean feat. Unless the program was designed with cross-platform compatibility in mind at the start, creating a second version of the program for *Linux* (for example) would be a substantial undertaking. Even if successful, the real work would begin after the program is released, and the bug reports and user questions begin rolling in!

Fortunately, for the past 15 years there's been a vigorous project in the open-source community to help solve this problem. The fruit of their work is an application that lets us run *Windows* programs on Unix-style operating systems (such as *Linux*) without having to make any changes to the programs themselves. The project is called *Wine*, a recursive acronym that means *Wine* Is Not an Emulator. (If you've never come across a recursive acronym before, just spend some time with your neighborhood computer geek.)

Wine isn't perfect, and there are many *Windows* applications that don't run very well on *Wine*. But fortunately, *EchoLink* runs rather well. So one solution for running *EchoLink* on *Linux* is to install *Wine*. It has become a standard part of most *Linux* distributions, so you might find that it is already installed on your system. Once *Wine* is ready to go, you can download the *EchoLink* installer package, and then run the setup using *Wine*. When the installer finishes, you should be able to run *EchoLink* by choosing its icon from the *Wine* sub-menu on your *Linux* desktop.

Wine is still under development, and the *EchoLink* team doesn't officially support it, but many *Linux* users have reported success running *EchoLink* on *Linux* using *Wine*. Most likely, as the project progresses, *Wine* compatibility will get even better.

Chapter 8

Under the Hood: *IRLP*

SOFTWARE ARCHITECTURE

IRLP is a collection of scripts, configuration files, and executable programs (called *binaries*) that work closely together. One of the strengths of the system is flexibility. Small pieces of the system may be updated as needed, and enterprising node owners can do a great deal of customization by modifying (or adding) scripts or binaries themselves.

The heart of the node software is the *Linux* implementation of the open-source VoIP program *Speak Freely. Speak Freely* handles the basic tasks in the lowest level of the voice-over-Internet conversation, such as the User Datagram Protocol (UDP) transport, buffering, compression and decompression, and management of the audio device (the sound card). The other programs and scripts are what make *IRLP* custom-engineered for Amateur Radio linking. These include programs that interact with the interface board (to operate the link transceiver and detect DTMF digits), and other *daemons* that run in the background to process connection requests and software updates. There is also a set of utility programs and scripts for testing the system and performing certain tasks manually, from the *Linux* command shell.

Although *IRLP* can be set up on an existing *Linux* installation, it's most commonly installed along with a custom distribution of *Linux* on a "clean" machine. There are two advantages to setting up *IRLP* this way: First, by installing *IRLP* and *Linux* at the same time from the same distribution, you can be sure the two are compatible versions of software that are designed to work together. Second, the *Linux* install shipped with the *IRLP* kit installs only the components of *Linux* that are required for *IRLP*, without unnecessary extras. This is particularly important if you are resurrecting an older PC for use as an *IRLP* machine, and want to make maximum use of the available hardware resources, such as disk space and RAM.

HARDWARE ARCHITECTURE

The only specialized hardware used by *IRLP* is the *IRLP* interface board (Figure 5.1). The interface board, which is provided by *IRLP* as part of the hardware/software kit, ties together the PC's parallel port, the input/output jacks of the sound card, and the link transceiver (or repeater). The board contains a DTMF decoder chip, and additional components for detecting the COS signal from the receiver and keying the PTT line of the transmitter. It uses the PC's parallel port to exchange commands and data with the software.

The board also provides three general-purpose auxiliary output pins which can be keyed on and off from the software. These are normally-open MOSFET outputs which can be switched to ground. For example, a custom DTMF script could be written that enables or disables a secondary receiver in response to commands sent over the link frequency.

The *SpeakFreely* module must (of course) communicate with the PC's sound card, and one of the *IRLP* hardware requirements is that a genuine Sound Blaster sound card be used. The *IRLP* Web site carries a complete list of the various Sound Blaster models that have been tested. Fortunately, the list of sound-card drivers for *Linux* is growing rapidly, and so may the list of supported sound cards. Creative Labs has released dozens of Sound Blaster models over the years, so finding a compatible sound card for your machine shouldn't be a problem.

GETTING CONNECTED

An *IRLP* QSO begins when a station in range of one node, call it Node A, punches in the four-digit node number of the station he'd like to connect to, using his DTMF pad. These tones are picked up by the node's link transceiver, and passed along to the audio input of the *IRLP* interface board. The board's DTMF decoder chip detects the dual-tone signals, converts them to the corresponding binary values (representing 0, 1, A, #, etc.), and sends them to the parallel port. *IRLP*'s DTMF program accepts this data from the parallel port and passes it as a string of ASCII digits to a script, which interprets the digits according to a list of rules.

If the script determines that this is a "connect" command (normally a four-digit sequence), it starts the process of locating the remote station and connecting to it over the Internet.

The first step in this process is to determine the remote node's IP address. Since IP addresses frequently change, the software consults a special DNS server to learn under which address this particular node is logged in. *IRLP* operates a set of several name servers that work as backups to each other. Even if no server is reachable for some reason, the software automatically falls back to a cached copy of the list in a local host's file.

Once the IP address is determined, communication between the nodes begins. The first order of business is a special message sent from Node A to Node B saying, in effect, "I'd like to connect to you — please respond." If Node B is open for business, it will have a program running in the background that is listening for connection requests such as this, and the request will be received and processed.

Now that the two nodes know that they want to connect to each other, they begin by authenticating each other. Each node has a copy of *IRLP*'s PGP *keyring* — the list of each node's public key — and, of course, its own private key. Using PGP (explained in detail in the next section), and a challenge-response conversation in both directions,

Node A and Node B each assure themselves that the other is legitimate.

Before firing up the VoIP link, there's one more order of business — to decide on a codec. *IRLP* supports both GSM and ADPCM. Although ADPCM is the default, if the calling node is configured to run GSM, the answering node will need to use GSM, too.

Finally, both stations start up their *Speak Freely* software, and now can begin exchanging VoIP signals. The QSO has begun!

During the QSO, the two nodes alternate between sending and receiving streams of VoIP packets. When the *IRLP* software on Node A detects an active COS signal, it tells *Speak Freely* to begin encoding audio from the sound card and shipping it off as a chain of packets to Node B over the Internet. The *Speak Freely* software on Node B, which has been eagerly awaiting the arrival of these packets, receives the first one in the chain and tells the *IRLP* software to key up the local link via PTT. Each incoming packet is parsed, decompressed, and sent to the sound card for playback. When the COS signal at Node A finally drops, the flow of packets ceases, and Node B releases PTT after a short delay.

The virtual connection between Node A and Node B remains "up" until one node or the other drops it, or until one node or the other stops responding. (This can happen if the Internet connection fails in the middle of a QSO.) Separately from the raw VoIP data, the nodes send *keep-alive* messages to each other periodically to be sure the other side is still able to respond.

PRETTY GOOD PRIVACY (PGP)

One of the lynchpins of *IRLP*'s security system is a mechanism called PGP, or Pretty Good Privacy. PGP is a data-security technique that can provide data privacy, integrity, and authentication. It's commonly used to prepare messages that move over the Internet from one computer to another, since none of these features is inherent in the Internet itself.

PGP uses two ingenious techniques for making this work. The first is called *public-key cryptography*. This is a method of encrypting a message so that the sender and receiver can keep its contents private, without the sender and receiver having agreed upon a *key* ahead of time. The second, which is related to it, is called *digital signing* — a way of verifying a message using a digital signature.

In cryptography, a key is somewhat like a password; given an encrypted message, the recipient can unlock (decrypt) the message if he knows the right key. Often, the same key is used to encrypt the message as to decrypt it. However, mathematicians have discovered that it's possible to create two completely different keys that work as a pair — one is used to encrypt the message, and the other is used to decrypt it. This is called a public-private key pair, because one key is usually freely advertised, while the other one is kept secret.

Here's how it works: The recipient of a message has a public-private key pair. Someone who wants to send him a message first asks him for his public key, which he freely gives out. The sender then uses the public key to encrypt a message, and sends the encrypted message to the recipient. After getting the message, the recipient decrypts it using his private key. Anyone who might have intercepted the message on its way to the recipient won't be able to make heads or tails of it, because the only way to decrypt it is to use the private key, which the recipient has kept secret.

Public-key cryptography requires a lot of number crunching, however, and long messages might take a long time for a computer to encrypt. So instead, public-key techniques are often used to help the sender and receiver securely exchange a shorter key that's used to encrypt and decrypt the actual message.

If this sounds like a lot of effort to go through, you might be surprised to learn that it happens every time you visit a "secure" Internet site with your Web browser. If you buy something through an online store and submit your credit card number, your Web browser first asks the Web site for its public key, which it uses to negotiate another key, called a *session key*, to encrypt your credit card number on its way through the Internet. The big benefit of this technique is that you don't need to make any prior arrangements with the Web site with which you're transacting — all of the negotiation occurs on the spot, yet the information is almost completely secure.

Behind the scenes, the Web site provided its public key in the form of a *digital certificate*. This is a special message that contains not only the Web site's public key, but also the name of the Web site (and the company that owns it), plus a digital signature. Your Web browser uses the digital signature to ensure that the public key truly belongs to the Web site it is trying to access.

But how? Once again, public-key cryptography saves the day. Each certificate is issued by a trusted company called a *certification authority* (CA), which verifies all of the Web site's information ahead of time, converts it all into a large, nearly-unique number called a *digest*, encrypts the digest with its own private key, then throws everything into a certificate which it gives to the Web site operator. (The encrypted digest is the digital signature.) When your Web browser receives the certificate, it computes the digest, then decrypts the certificate's signature (using the certification authority's public key), and compares the two digests. If they're the same, the Web browser — and you — are assured that the public key matches the Web site's name. Your browser also checks to see that the Web site's name, as claimed in the certificate, is correct.

So we return to PGP. Although a full-blown PGP implementation has all of these features available, the most important for an Amateur Radio application is authentication. This is the feature of PGP that is used by *IRLP* (**Figure 8.1**). When two *IRLP* nodes establish a connection, they exchange digitally signed messages. To authenticate itself, each node generates a random message, creates a "digest" of it, encrypts the digest with its private key (a process known as *signing*), and sends it to its partner. The partner verifies the signature by decrypting the digest with the sender's public key, and making sure it matches the message. If everything checks out, the partner can be reasonably certain of the sender's identity.

Although PGP can use digital certificates to exchange public keys, a simpler approach is to have each node keep a *keyring*, a list of every other node's number and public key. When your node is added to the *IRLP* network, your node number and

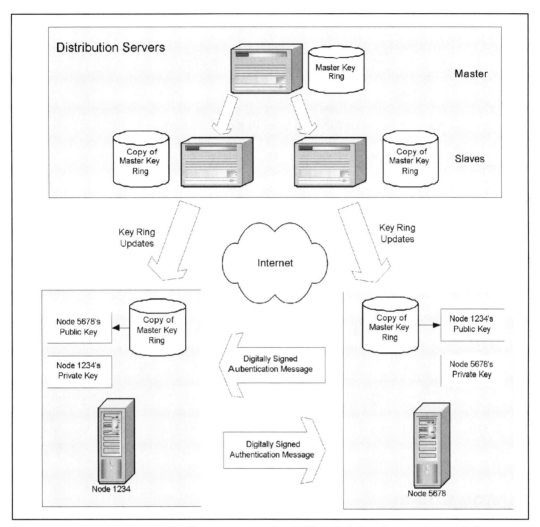

Figure 8.1 — The *IRLP* authentication process, using PGP digital signatures. Each node has a copy of the master key ring, which is a list of the public keys for each node on the network. The key ring is updated when new nodes join the system. Each node also stores its own private key, which it keeps secret.

public key is added to every other node's keyring by the *IRLP* system. In effect, the *IRLP* system, by distributing your new public key, is assuring other *IRLP* nodes that you are who you say you are, whenever your *IRLP* node connects to another over the Internet. This is similar to the role of the CA in the secure Web conversation described earlier.

SOFTWARE UPDATES

If you're running an *IRLP* node, one thing you can be sure of is that the *IRLP* software is always up to date. That's because *IRLP* is designed to "phone home" each night, check to see if any new software is available, and if so, to download it and install it.

To keep the updates efficient (and reliable), they're distributed across a set of synchronized "slave" servers, rather than just one. Each node's IRLP software selects an appropriate server from the list of the ones online, and then logs into that server to receive the updates. Distributing the load in this fashion helps ensure that the system will "scale" well as the number of nodes continues to grow.

Most of the time, the only thing that needs updating are the database files — the master list of nodes and addresses on the system, and the corresponding master keyring with each node's public key. Each node also keeps an updated copy of the "connect" and "disconnect" audio messages for every other node, since the node originating the connection plays them over the local link. For the most part, these updates execute swiftly and silently, without the need for periodic maintenance.

One useful feature of these nightly updates is that every IRLP node carries with it all of the necessary information to establish a connection with every other node, without the continuous need for a central server. Although the odds are slim that each and every slave server would be unavailable, the IRLP software is designed to fall back to local files if none of the main servers is reachable. The only nodes not contactable in that scenario would be those whose IP address had changed recently, or those that had just been added to the system since the last nightly update.

The nightly updates are scheduled and kicked off by a *Linux* daemon called cron. cron can also be used to run custom scripts on custom schedules. For example, you could set up your own crontab entries to enable and disable your node at certain times of day, or to automatically connect and disconnect to other nodes or reflectors. cron is simple but very flexible.

CUSTOM SCRIPTS

After installing *IRLP*, you'll find that the installer has created a directory called **/home/irlp/custom**. This is the place to put any custom scripts you create, to keep them separate from the "stock" scripts and binaries supplied with the *IRLP* package. This keeps everything organized, and helps ensure that the periodic automatic software updates don't affect your customizations.

Although scripts for *IRLP* can be written in a variety of different languages, such as *Perl*, it's most commonly done as a *shell script*. A shell script is a script that's executed by the *command shell*, the same program that accepts your commands from the keyboard. Unix-like systems such as *Linux* can use any of several different shells, but the default for *Linux* is **bash** (which stands for "Bourne-again shell," since its language is compatible with the Bourne shell). The first line of each script is a special comment that indicates which program should interpret the script.

```
#!/bin/bash

. /home/irlp/custom/environment          # Set up the shell environment.

$BIN/key                                 # Begin transmitting.

usleep 2000                              # Wait 2 seconds.

$BIN/play $AUDIO/$1.wav >&/dev/null 2>&1  # Play the WAV file, and wait till
                                           finished.

$BIN/unkey                               # Release the PTT.
```

Figure 8.2—A simple *IRLP* shell script.

An example of a simple *IRLP* shell script is shown in **Figure 8.2**. This script keys the link transmitter, plays a WAV file through the sound card (and over the link), and then un-keys. The script takes one argument, namely, the name of the WAV file (without the extension).

Of course, to really be useful, the script could be enhanced to check to be sure the link is neither transmitting nor receiving before playing the sound, and either to exit or to wait until the transmission is complete.

To create a new script, use a text editor (such as vi or pico) to build a text file containing the script commands, and then mark the file as executable using the *chmod* command. Ideally, you should mark the file as owner-executable, and change the owner of the file to repeater, the username under which *IRLP* utilities run, using chown.

For example:

cd /home/irlp/custom

pico myscript   [edit the file, save it, and exit]

chmod 750 myscript

chown repeater myscript

One special script in the custom directory is custom decode. This is the place to put the codes for any custom DTMF functions you'd like to implement. Each time a sequence of DTMF digits is received, the *IRLP* software calls this script. The script can compare the incoming DTMF string against any number of special combinations, and if found, take some sort of action in response. The software checks the script's exit code to determine whether to run default processing on the DTMF sequence. If the exit code is 0, it means (presumably) that the digits didn't match any of the custom functions, and should be acted on by the main *IRLP* decode script. If the exit code is 1, processing of the digits terminates without further action. **Figure 8.3** shows an example of custom decode. If you're planning to create your own version of custom decode, note that the star is encoded as the letter S, the pound sign comes over as P,

```
#!/bin/bash

# This is the custom decode file. Make sure all valid codes exit with "exit 1".

# Standard enable/disable codes.
if [ "$1" = "12001" ] ; then "$SCRIPT"/disable ; exit 1 ; fi
if [ "$1" = "12002" ] ; then "$SCRIPT"/enable ; exit 1 ; fi

# Key and un-key the AUX1 output of the interface board.
if [ "$1" = "*711" ] ; then "$BIN"/aux1on ; exit 1 ; fi
if [ "$1" = "*710" ] ; then "$BIN"/aux1off ; exit 1 ; fi

exit 0
```

Figure 8.3—Example of a custom_decode script.

and the D digit cannot be used.

With the right combination of scripts and binaries, you can do just about anything. The binaries provided with *IRLP* (in the **/home/irlp/bin** directory) take care of interacting with the interface board and the VoIP system, but if you're familiar with programming, you can certainly create your own binaries to drive other peripherals that might be connected.

Taken to an extreme, one interesting (and useful) project would be a full-blown repeater controller that runs on *Linux* and interfaces with receivers, transmitters, and other equipment through the computer's serial, parallel, or USB ports. The program could even handle remote control and autopatch through voice-modem devices, and the whole thing could be built with *IRLP* baked right in from the beginning! As you can see, the possibilities — just like our Amateur Radio project lists — are virtually endless.

For more examples of custom *IRLP* scripts, check the *IRLP* node owner's group on *Yahoo!* Many of these scripts are fully refined and might be ready to run on your own system without modification.

LOGGING

As it runs, *IRLP* generates a detailed log file of all significant activity. Logs are maintained as ordinary text files in the /home/irlp/log directory. The current log file is called messages, and previous log files are renamed to messages.1, messages.2, and so on. A portion of a typical *IRLP* log file is shown in **Figure 8.4**.

An easy way to keep running tabs on your node's activity is to open up a virtual terminal session and enter this command:

tail –f /home/irlp/log/messages

This will display the last 10 lines of the current log file, and continuously update the display as new log entries are added.

```
Oct 04 2003 16:17:19 -0400 Node Enabled
Oct 04 2003 22:58:18 -0400 IRLP call initiated to stn4200
Oct 04 2003 22:58:23 -0400 stn420 reply connectok ADPCM
Oct 04 2003 22:59:06 -0400 Node Disconnect from stn4200
Oct 04 2003 22:59:49 -0400 busy stn4579
Oct 05 2003 17:07:59 -0400 stn5562 connect ADPCM
Oct 05 2003 17:08:42 -0400 stn5562 disconnect
Oct 05 2003 22:52:53 -0400 IRLP call initiated to stn4130
Oct 05 2003 22:52:59 -0400 stn413 reply connectok ADPCM
Oct 05 2003 22:53:11 -0400 Node Disconnect from stn4130
Oct 06 2003 21:13:02 -0400 decode: DTMF = 9990
Oct 06 2003 21:13:04 -0400 Node Connected to reflector echo on channel 0
Oct 06 2003 21:13:45 -0400 decode: DTMF = 73
Oct 06 2003 21:13:46 -0400 Node Disconnect from ref9990
Oct 06 2003 22:40:44 -0400 decode: DTMF = 5406
Oct 06 2003 22:40:45 -0400 IRLP call initiated to stn5406
Oct 06 2003 22:40:50 -0400 stn5406 reply connectok ADPCM
Oct 06 2003 22:41:51 -0400 decode: DTMF = 73
Oct 06 2003 22:41:52 -0400 Node Disconnect from stn5406
```

Figure 8.4—A portion of a typical *IRLP* log file.

ECHOIRLP

When *EchoLink* and *IRLP* emerged as the two major Amateur Radio linking systems a few years ago, many node owners naturally wondered whether there was a way to set up a single PC that could function both as an *IRLP* node and as an *EchoLink* node. Certainly, it seems like a shame to have to set up two separate PCs and two separate interfaces — not to mention two separate sets of radio gear — just to provide access to both systems at the same site.

A few enterprising hams worked on this problem, and came up with a solution built around two software packages that had already been built: *IRLP* and *theBridge*. The project is known as *EchoIRLP*. Today, about 300 of the world's *IRLP* and *EchoLink* nodes are running the *EchoIRLP* package, so it has clearly been a success.

EchoIRLP is not a bridge between the two systems, as you might first believe, but rather a dual-mode system that can switch between one network and the other. A typical *EchoIRLP* node is ready to accept incoming connections from *EchoLink* nodes or *IRLP* nodes, and can make outgoing calls to either system, just not at the same time.

An *EchoIRLP* node actually begins its life as an ordinary *IRLP* node; the first part of the setup procedure is the same. This means that an *EchoIRLP* node is running a distribution of the *Linux* operating system (CentOS), along with the *IRLP* software and the custom *IRLP* interface board. But after the *IRLP* node is up and running and fully configured and adjusted, the node owner can add *EchoLink* capability by downloading and installing the *EchoIRLP* software. Most of the action happens inside of a special release of *theBridge* conference bridge, which is glued together with the existing *IRLP* modules by a set of scripts. *theBridge* handles the details of connecting to nodes on the EchoLink network, in very much the same way it manages *EchoLink* conferences. But internally, *theBridge* and *IRLP* are "wired" together so that audio packets received from an EchoLink node are routed through *SpeakFreely* and the computer's sound card, out to the transmitter, and vice versa.

Since an *EchoIRLP* node is logged in to both networks at once, it shows up as both an *EchoLink* node and as an *IRLP* node in the logged-in node listings on each system. Usually, the node has a different node number on the *IRLP* side than it has on the *EchoLink* side. Just like the conventional *EchoLink* software, an *EchoIRLP* node can accept more than one *EchoLink* connection at the same time in roundtable fashion, but still respects the one-to-one rule on *IRLP*. In fact, when the node is connected to another node on one network, its status shows up as "busy" on the other.

EMBEDDED *IRLP*

When setting up a new Internet linking node, a natural question to ask is whether there's a way to install a node that runs as a "black box," not requiring a PC. After all, a PC is typically a large, power-hungry machine that might seem like overkill for running a VoIP link, and PCs don't exactly have a stellar record of reliability.

Fortunately, there's a good *embedded* solution for *IRLP*. Instead of installing an *IRLP* interface board in a conventional PC, you can order a complete *IRLP*-Embedded computer, which is really a small, custom-made PC that comes ready-to-run either *IRLP* or *EchoIRLP*. As you can see from **Figure 8.5**, the whole thing fits in a small package that includes a tiny motherboard, memory, and an *IRLP* interface board. This kind of approach has a lot of advantages over a PC, particularly if you're expecting to install it at a remote repeater site:

No hard drive. The typical, mechanical hard drive is one of the few moving parts in a conventional PC, and one of its major points of failure. The Embedded *IRLP* box has no hard drive at all; instead, it boots *Linux* from a flash device, and loads software into a RAM drive for fast access. This gives you higher reliability, less noise, and lower power consumption.

No internal power supply. The whole thing runs from an external 12-volt power source, rather than using a conventional switching power supply that runs from AC.

This means you can run the whole site from a single DC power source, including the radio or repeater and the embedded computer. The box draws only about 14 watts on average, much less than a typical PC.

All-internal wiring. Because it's a custom-made device, there is no external parallel-port cable as you would normally find in a PC-based IRLP node, and no external audio jack wiring to a sound card. Instead, all connections to the radio or repeater are through a single DB-9 connector.

Figure 8.5 — The Embedded *IRLP* solution.

Chapter 9

Asterisk and *app_rpt*

If you've kept up with the major projects in the open-source community, you've probably come across *Asterisk*. The *Asterisk* PBX has earned a reputation as a respectable substitute for the traditional business phone system, which until recently was typically an expensive "black box" without much flexibility. Compared to other phone systems, *Asterisk* has a lot of advantages. It runs on a conventional, inexpensive PC. The *Asterisk* software is free (free as in beer *and* free as in speech), and runs on a free operating system (*Linux*). It is endlessly configurable, offering plenty of built-in flexibility as well as a wide variety of plug-in options. In fact, *Asterisk* is so flexible that it's become a platform for both commercial and Amateur Radio VoIP systems. This chapter describes just such a system.

Unlike some of the other equipment and software described in this book, an *Asterisk*-based VoIP system is more like a toolkit than a ready-to-run machine. If you learn how to use the tools, you can create a system that does exactly what you need. But learning the ins and outs of the toolbox might take some time, especially if you haven't fiddled with open-source software very much, so expect to devote some extra effort to an *Asterisk*-based VoIP system. You might find that it's time well spent, since you're likely to learn plenty about *Linux* along the way, and end up with a custom-designed solution that works exactly the way you want it to.

Flexibility is the biggest advantage of the "toolkit" approach. With a system built around *Asterisk*, you can build a node that's part of a larger, public VoIP network, or you can set up a private VoIP link for a special purpose. One example is a set of point-to-point links that join two or three remote receivers in a wide-area repeater system. Another might be a remote-base-style system that lets you jump on a distant repeater using a low-power handheld transceiver around the house. **Figure 9-1** shows some of the possibilities for Internet linking using *Asterisk*.

A VOICE SWITCH

A PC running *Asterisk* is a modern version of the clicking, whirring mountain of relays and circuit boards known as a *private branch exchange*, or PBX. The PBX is essentially a switch that can route telephone calls between an office full of telephones and a set of lines provided by the phone company. The PBX lets workers in the office make calls to each other, as well as incoming and outgoing calls to and from the outside world.

The job of a PBX is a little more complicated these days, since telephone calls are carried over a combination of voice and digital circuits — the conventional twisted pair (sometimes called POTS, an acronym for Plain Old Telephone Service) and VoIP. A computerized switch is a natural choice for VoIP, since all of the routing and switching can be handled in software. It can also work with POTS lines, as long as it's equipped with adapters that can translate between analog and digital signals.

In *Asterisk*-speak, optional software modules are called *applications*, with short, unpronounceable names beginning with *app_*. The key application for Amateur Radio linking on *Asterisk* is *app_rpt*. The *app_rpt* application sits between the *Asterisk* core and the hardware interface to the radio equipment, handling radio-related functions such as carrier detect, frequency control, and transmitter control (PTT).

The *app_rpt* application is the centerpiece of a system called TIARA, which

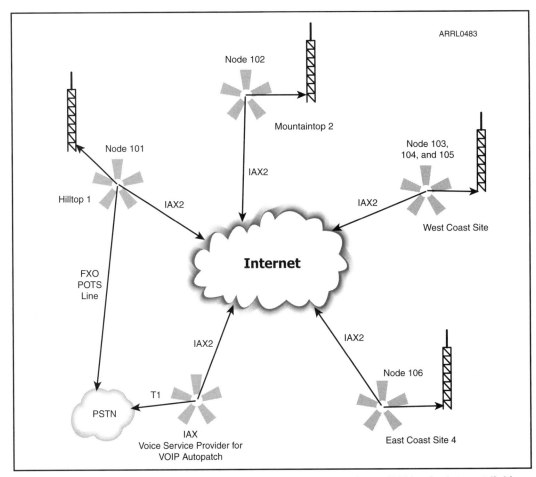

Figure 9.1 — The *Asterisk* system with *app_rpt* provides plenty of possibilities for Internet linking, as well as full-featured repeater control.

stands for "Technology Implemented by *App_Rpt / Asterisk*." The TIARA project aims to provide a whole host of radio-related functions on the *Asterisk* platform. With the right configuration, the system can be used as a full-blown repeater controller, a remote-base controller, or a VoIP Internet link. TIARA can take advantage of *Asterisk's* software-based DTMF decoder to handle commands sent over-the-air or from an incoming phone call, and remote control of the system over the Internet. Since all of the software is open source — from the *Linux* operating system all the way up — anyone familiar with programming can jump in and make custom changes, improvements, and enhancements.

NODES, LINKS, AND CHANNELS

It's important to remember that when you're building a repeater linking system around *Asterisk* and *app_rpt*, you're creating a complete repeater controller, not just an Internet link. The system can either be operated by itself as a stand-alone repeater, or connected to over the Internet from other nodes that are similarly equipped.

Unlike a typical repeater controller, an *Asterisk*-based system has all of the repeater control functions running in software, rather than hardware. Just as when *Asterisk* is functioning as a telephone switch, virtually all of the audio that travels through the system is handled digitally, rather than as analog signals. It's the job of the interface device to convert analog signals to and from digital, and this happens at the earliest and latest possible points along the path. The big advantage of this technique is that changing the node's "personality" is just a matter of updating its software, rather than having to make difficult and potentially costly hardware changes. It also means that very complicated switching and bridging arrangements can be set up quickly and easily, again without touching the hardware.

Another important term in the *Asterisk* vocabulary is *channel*. Channels are the endpoints of communication: a telephone set, a telephone line, or a radio transceiver, as examples. Each different kind of channel has a separate software module (called a *channel driver*) that "knows" how to handle a certain technology. Inside the *Asterisk* software, two or more channels can be bridged to one another, establishing a connection that allows two-way communication. Each type of channel has a configuration file that sets up the options for the channel, and specifies how certain kinds of events on the channel should be handled.

The next piece of the puzzle is the *dialplan*, which is a kind of recipe or roadmap for how the various channels should interact. Although the term is a carryover from the world of telephones, not every item in a dialplan is something that actually needs to be "dialed," nor do any of the channels have to be telephone-related. Instead, a dialplan can describe (for example) what should happen when a VoIP connection request is received from another node over the Internet. *Asterisk* has a rich set of commands that can be invoked in the dialplan, somewhat like a computer programming language.

INTERFACING

For connecting radio equipment to *Asterisk*, there are a couple of options. The first-class approach is the Quad PCI Radio Interface, available from QRV Communications (**qrvc.com**). As the name implies, this is an adapter that fits inside the computer in a peripheral component interconnect (PCI) slot, and provides interface ports for up to four transmit/receive devices (**Figure 9-2**). Each port has an audio input, an audio output, a COS line, and a PTT line. The audio input and COS lines connect to a receiver, and the audio output and PTT lines connect to a transmitter. Of course, if a transceiver is being used, all four lines connect to the transceiver, since it is providing both functions at once.

Figure 9.2 — The Quad PCI Radio Interface.

Figure 9.3 — His Eminence, the Fob.

Another option is a device called the USB Radio Interface (URI), affectionately known as the USB Fob (**Figure 9-3**), or the Dongle. The URI (from DMK Engineering, **dmkeng.com**) connects to the PC's USB port and provides connections to a single transmitter/receiver. It is built around a single chip, the C-Media CM108, that acts as a USB sound "card" with extra input/output lines that are used for the PTT and COS connections. A companion channel driver lets the URI play nicely with *Asterisk*. With this arrangement, DTMF digits received over the air are decoded in software using *Asterisk's* own DSP-based decoder.

THE ALLSTAR LINK SYSTEM

If you've set up an Amateur *Asterisk* system with *app_rpt*, you're invited to add your node to the list of nodes on the AllStar Link network. Just as with other linking systems such as *EchoLink* and *IRLP*, each node on the network is assigned a node number, and nodes can be connected to one another by using DTMF commands on a portable or mobile radio within range of the node's repeater or remote base.

An AllStar Link node requires some extra software to join the network. The easiest way to set up a complete *Asterisk/app_rpt* system for the AllStar system is to download and burn a single CD-ROM that includes a copy of the CentOS distribution of *Linux* and a complete *Asterisk* installation. This downloadable image is available from the AllStar Link Web site (**allstarlink.org**). The Web site also has information about how to request an AllStar Link node number.

One key difference between a repeater node on the AllStar Link system and a repeater node on another system such as *EchoLink* or *IRLP* is that the *Asterisk* box functions as both the repeater controller and the Internet link — the two functions are completely integrated into a single controller. In contrast, *EchoLink* and *IRLP* repeater nodes are typically either hard-wired to a dedicated repeater controller, or placed at a location separate from the repeater and joined to the repeater itself over the air. You can think of a system like the AllStar network as a worldwide collection of repeater controllers that live on the Internet.

Choosing a PC

Just as with other kinds of linking systems, it's worth giving some advance thought to what kind of PC you will use to host the system. For an *Asterisk/app_rpt* installation, this consideration is even more critical, since the PC will be hosting the repeater itself, not just the Internet link. Reliability is the number-one consideration; as long as the machine has sufficient memory and minimally adequate CPU speed, it will hum along just fine; the latest top-of-the-line dual-core screamer is probably not the best choice.

If the site is not easily accessible, consider using an embedded PC that is rack-mountable and can run from a single-sided 12-volt power supply. Just one PCI slot is required (if using the PCI Quad Radio Interface card), so you can easily use a small machine that draws modest power and generates minimal heat. Some embedded PCs have no moving parts at all (no fan or hard drive), leaving them with many fewer things that can go wrong in the middle of the night at the top of a mountain in the dead of winter.

INSTALLATION

There are several ways to set up an *app_rpt* machine for use on the AllStar Link network, but the easiest is to download and run the Allstar CentOS Install Disk (ACID). ACID is a complete image of the CentOS *Linux* distribution, along with the latest *Asterisk* package, *app_rpt*, and the appropriate configuration files. You can download the ACID CD-ROM ISO image from the **allstarlink.org** Web site, and burn it on to a blank CD. Be sure to also download and print a copy of the installation instructions and the System Administrators guide; these will walk you through the installation and configuration steps to get you up and running quickly.

But before running the installer, if you're expecting to add your node to the AllStar network, you'll need an AllStar link node number. Node numbers can be requested from the **allstarlink.org** Web site. When you run the ACID installer, you'll be prompted to enter your new node number and password near the end of the installation process. The install script automatically stores this information in the appropriate *Asterisk* configuration files before it starts up *Asterisk* for the first time. There is also an option to run a small program that reports the status of your node to the **allstarlink.org** Web site periodically.

Once the installation is finished and the machine is running with its newly-configured software, the next step is to connect and adjust the equipment. For either the Quad PCI interface card or the URI, you'll need to put together a custom-made cable to connect the radio gear to the *Asterisk* interface. The Quad PCI interface has RJ-45 (modular) connectors, and the URI has a 25-pin computer-type connector. For some radio-interface combinations, you may need a few additional components (such as switching transistors and resistors) mounted on a small circuit board between the interface and the rig. For example, the URI has an open-collector output for the PTT line that goes to ground when the PTT is activated; if your equipment expects the reverse of this sense, you'll need to add a simple inverter stage between the URI and the transmitter. The documentation for either interface has detailed pin-outs and schematics, which should be followed carefully.

The main adjustment step is to set the audio levels to and from the radio. Although you can do a rough adjustment by ear, the most accurate deviation adjustments require a service monitor. The *Asterisk/app_rpt* software packages have functions that will generate test tones at specific reference levels to make this easier. Audio-level adjustment might involve a combination of hardware and software adjustments; in particular, the Quad PCI interface has multi-turn trimpots for each of the four radio ports directly on the PCI card. All of the audio adjustments for the URI device are handled in software.

LINKING FROM A PC

The *Asterisk* package supports several different standard VoIP protocols, such as Session Initiation Protocol (SIP). Thanks to standards such as SIP, it's possible to use various non-*Asterisk* programs and devices to connect over the Internet to an *Asterisk*-based system. For example, you can use an IP phone, which resembles a conventional telephone, but is actually a complete digital voice terminal with an Ethernet connector instead of a conventional twisted-pair port. Or, you can use any number of desktop PC applications that emulate the functions of an IP phone.

But there's a catch: These IP devices and programs are designed to work like conventional, full-duplex telephones. They're not a good fit for the Amateur Radio world, which is predominantly half-duplex. What's missing is a push-to-talk switch — a convenient way to take control of a half-duplex link to make a brief transmission.

Fortunately, there's a desktop PC application called *iaxRPT* that solves this problem. IAX stands for Inter-Asterisk eXchange (pronounced "eeks"); it's an Internet protocol specifically designed to connect *Asterisk*-based systems to one another. The *iaxRPT* program, which is offered as a free download from **www.xelatec.com/xipar/iarpt** can connect to a remote system running *Asterisk* and *app_rpt* using IAX2 to carry on a remote QSO. At first glance it resembles a typical "soft phone" application, but it also handles the all-important PTT function, and it's built expressly for working with *app_rpt*.

When setting up your *Asterisk/app_rpt* node, the installer creates a couple of configuration files on the machine (iax_rpt_custom.conf and extensions_rpt_custom.conf) that set up the server side of the link. When you install *iaxRPT* on another computer, you'll be prompted to enter the matching information (node number and password, for example) to let you connect remotely to your own node. Once everything is up and running, you can hook up to your repeater or remote base from anywhere in the world, and carry on a QSO using the desktop computer's microphone and speakers. The **CTRL** key on the keyboard works as the push-to-talk switch; press it to begin speaking, release it to stop.

Chapter 10

Remote Control Techniques

In the US, FCC rules allow nearly any Amateur station to be remotely controlled over a *control link*, which joins the *control point* to the station. The two types of links that the Part 97 rules allow are an auxiliary (radio) link, and *wireline*. Wireline typically means a telephone-line connection of some kind, even a part-time connection such as a single phone call, and even over the broader public telephone network that includes cellular phones.

IVR REMOTE CONTROL

Certainly, a convenient way to fulfill the control-link requirement would be to have some way to place a telephone call to the link and send it DTMF commands, perhaps even with automated voice responses. In the world of telephone systems, these kinds of setups are called *integrated voice response systems*, or IVRs for short. It's the same technology you bump into when you call for help with your telephone or cable TV service.

Fortunately, in the world of Internet linking, there are a couple of different ways to make this happen. If you are running an *EchoLink* node (in Sysop mode), and your computer is equipped with a *voice modem*, you can connect a spare telephone line to your computer and get a ready-to-run IVR right out of the box! There's also an interesting way to use the *Asterisk* software package (on *Linux*) to build a custom IVR to control an *IRLP* node. Both techniques are described in the following sections.

ECHOLINK DIAL-IN REMOTE CONTROL

On *EchoLink's* Sysop Setup screen, on the Remt tab, there's an option to enable dial-in remote control. If your PC has a voice modem installed, this option can be enabled to provide dial-in IVR remote control of your node. Although a voice modem is an inexpensive device, be aware that most modems are *not* voice modems. The difference is that while a conventional modem lets you exchange data over a telephone line, a voice modem (as the name implies) adds voice features that let the computer send and receive audio streams directly. With the proper software, the voice modem allows the PC to play WAV files or synthesized speech to a caller, or to record a caller's speech. These, along with DTMF detection, are the key hardware ingredients for a PC-based IVR. In fact, many voice modems come with *Windows* software that turns your PC into a computerized answering machine.

On the Remt tab, choose the voice modem device and check the box to enable the dial-in remote control feature. It's also a good idea to set a passcode (for example, a four-digit number) to ensure proper security. Once this is set up, you should be able to dial the phone number on which the voice modem is connected, and do basic node control functions using the DTMF pad on your phone — from anywhere in the world. After entering the passcode at the beginning, a dial-in remote-control session is just like entering commands over the air. The only important difference is that you must press the pound key (#) after each command to indicate the end of the command, since there's no carrier to drop. A typical remote-control session might go like this:

[ringing sound]
PC: EchoLink … K-1-R-F-D-Link
You: 1-2-3-4 (the passcode)
PC: Enabled.
You: 1-9-3-8-#
PC: Connecting to G-B-3-B-N-Repeater...Connected.

If the Audio Monitor box was checked, you'll be able to hear any QSO in progress over the node when you dial in. When you're finished, you can just hang up, and *EchoLink* will drop the line after hearing no commands from you in a while.

If the telephone line and the voice modem both support Caller ID, the caller's name and telephone number will appear in the System log. This is a good way to audit the security of your dial-in remote control system.

If you don't happen to have a spare telephone line at the *EchoLink* node location, you have a couple of options. One possibility is to share an existing phone line with *EchoLink*. This isn't a perfect solution, of course, but at least you can set up EchoLink so it doesn't answer the line before you have a chance to pick up the phone yourself. Set the "Answer on n rings" value to a large number, such as 10.

An easy way to add a second telephone line is to use a VoIP phone service, such as Vonage, that provides a *voice terminal* with their service. The voice terminal is a small box that connects to your existing Internet connection and provides one or two modular jacks designed to be connected to conventional analog telephones. This jack (or jacks) acts in most respects like an ordinary "POTS" phone line, so it can be connected to your voice modem for *EchoLink* remote control without interfering in any way with your regular phone service.

IRLP REMOTE CONTROL WITH *ASTERISK*

The open-source movement has provided us with a broad range of tremendously useful software tools, including plenty of goodies useful to Amateur Radio. In

Chapter 9, we introduced *Asterisk*, a package that is typically used to create a private branch exchange (PBX), or telephone switch. But it has another very useful function — as an IVR. With the right configuration, you can put *Asterisk* to work as a complete wireline control system for your *IRLP* node. A big plus here is that no conventional telephone line is required; an Internet VoIP service provider can be used in its place, with no hardware required other than a conventional PC, such as the computer on which you're running *IRLP*.

The first step is to learn a little about *Asterisk* and how its *dialplans* work. A dial-plan is a roadmap for how Asterisk should handle an incoming call. To build an IVR with *Asterisk*, you'll be putting together a dialplan that tells the software to perform these steps whenever a call comes in:

1. Answer the call.
2. Play a short greeting message.
3. Accept the DTMF security code from the caller.
4. Play a short message indicating that the system is ready to accept commands.
5. Accept a DTMF command and perform its action.
6. Continue accepting commands until finished (go to step 5).
7. Hang up the call.

A big part of *Asterisk's* flexibility is its ability to work with other programs, including programs and scripts you write yourself. *Asterisk* has a couple of different protocols for working with external programs. One of these is the Asterisk Gateway Interface protocol, or AGI. Just like the Common Gateway Interface (CGI) for Web servers, AGI uses the system's standard-input and standard-output streams to provide the two-way pipe between *Asterisk* and the outboard program or script. There's also a variation of AGI called FastAGI, which uses a TCP/IP socket interface as the "pipe" instead of standard-input and standard-output. The main advantage of using a socket interface is that your homebrew program can keep running all the time and wait for work to do, rather than having to be launched by *Asterisk* each time a call comes in. This is friendlier for certain kinds of programs (and programming languages), and makes AGI, well, fast! Another benefit of using TCP/IP is that your FastAGI program doesn't even need to be on the same computer as *Asterisk*, since TCP/IP is a network protocol that works over local networks as well as the Internet.

For an *IRLP* remote control system, you can set up *Asterisk* to start up a custom program immediately after step 4 above. This program takes over where the dialplan leaves off — it accepts a command from the caller, takes some kind of action, and continues until the caller is finished. Then it exits, returning control back to the dialplan, where *As-*

```
[incoming]

exten => s,1,Answer( )

exten => s,2,Wait(1)

exten => s,3,Background(agent-pass)

exten => 1234,1,Playback(auth-thankyou)

exten => 1234,n,Agi(agi://localhost/irlp.agi)

exten => 1234,n,Hangup()
```

Figure 10.1

terisk finishes by hanging up the call.

A portion of a sample *Asterisk* dialplan (`extensions.conf`) for a simple IVR is shown in **Figure 10.1**. In this example, we imagine that the passcode for getting into the IVR is 1234.

To go with this dialplan, we use two messages from the standard set of greetings available in the *Asterisk* package (`agent-pass` and `auth-thankyou`), but of course you can record and use your own.

When the caller enters the correct passcode (1234), *Asterisk* treats this as an "extension" and launches the FastAGI program `irlp.agi`. In this example, `irlp.agi` is on the same machine as *Asterisk*, but if *Asterisk* and *IRLP* are on separate servers, install the FastAGI program on the *IRLP* box and use its host name in the agi URL instead of `localhost`.

Asterisk passes control of the call to `irlp.agi` and waits until it returns. While `irlp.agi` runs, it interacts with *Asterisk* by receiving DTMF command sequences and playing voice prompts in response.

A Google search will turn up useful frameworks that make it easy to write *FastAGI* programs in various programming languages. Although I'm fond of using *Java* for more complex *Asterisk* IVRs, I put together a simple *IRLP* control program using *Perl*. A package called *Asterisk::FastAGI*, available from the CPAN repository, lets you build your *FastAGI* code as a *Perl* module, and then run it as a server to manage the conversation between *Asterisk* and your own program.

Figure 10.2 shows a *FastAGI Perl* module for controlling an *IRLP* node. It simply accepts strings of DTMF digits from the caller and passes them to *IRLP's* DTMF detection script (`decode`), just as if the digits had been received over the air on the local link. A script like this gives system administrators remote access to all of the DTMF-controllable functions of their *IRLP* node from any telephone (or cell phone) anywhere in the world, no matter what might be happening on the link input at the time.

In this script, you'll notice that the `stream_file()` method plays a sound file back to the caller. For this script, I created two custom sound files (`irlp-ivr/thanks` and `irlp-ivr/hangup`), but you can of course use any of the standard sound files that ship with *Asterisk*. If you are running *Asterisk* and *IRLP* on two different machines, keep in mind that these sound files are stored on the *Asterisk* machine, not the *IRLP* machine.

To run this script on the *IRLP* box, be sure that *Perl* and the *Asterisk::FastAGI* packages are installed, then start it up with a short script like **Figure 10.3**.

At this point, you can use an *Asterisk* dialplan such as the one introduced earlier to invoke your *FastAGI* script when a telephone call is received.

WEB-BASED REMOTE CONTROL

Another convenient way to remotely control your node is to set up a Web-based control link. In this arrangement, you add special-purpose Web server software to the machine, and create a custom set of HTML pages for it. These pages would typically

```perl
package irlpAGI;

use base 'Asterisk::FastAGI';

sub irlp {
  my $self = shift;
  $callerid = $self->input('callerid');
  warn "Dial-in call from $callerid\n";

  while (true) {
    $digit_string = "";
    while (true) {
      $digit_num = $self->agi->wait_for_digit("10000");
      if ($digit_num == -1 or $digit_num == 0) {
        warn "Timeout or error; disconnecting\n";
        return;
      }
      if ($digit_num eq "") {
        warn "Null digit detected; hangup assumed\n";
        return;
      }
      $digit = "" . chr($digit_num);
      warn "Received digit: [$digit]\n";
      if ($digit_num eq "35" or $digit_num == 35 or $digit eq "#") {
        last;
      }
      $digit_string .= $digit;
    }
    if ($digit_string eq "") {
        last;
    }
    warn "Processing digit string: [$digit_string]\n";
    system("decode $digit_string");
    warn "Digit string processed.\n";
    $self->agi->stream_file("irlp-ivr/thanks");
  }
  warn "End of session\n";
  $self->agi->stream_file("irlp-ivr/hangup");
}

1;
```

Figure 10.2

```perl
#!/usr/bin/perl

use irlpAGI;


my $server = irlpAGI->new({
        port => '4573',
        user => 'repeater',
        group => 'repeater'
});


$server->run;
```

Figure 10.3

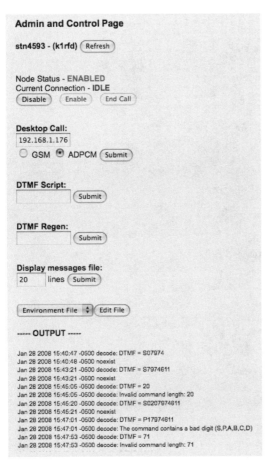

Admin and Control Page

stn4593 - (k1rfd) (Refresh)

Node Status - ENABLED
Current Connection - IDLE
(Disable) (Enable)   (End Call)

Desktop Call:
192.168.1.176
○ GSM ● ADPCM (Submit)

DTMF Script:
(Submit)

DTMF Regen:
(Submit)

Display messages file:
20   lines (Submit)

(Environment File ◆)(Edit File)

----- OUTPUT -----

Jan 28 2008 15:40:47 -0500 decode: DTMF = S07974
Jan 28 2008 15:40:48 -0500 noexist
Jan 28 2008 15:43:21 -0500 decode: DTMF = S7974611
Jan 28 2008 15:43:21 -0500 noexist
Jan 28 2008 15:45:05 -0500 decode: DTMF = 20
Jan 28 2008 15:45:05 -0500 decode: Invalid command length: 20
Jan 28 2008 15:46:20 -0500 decode: DTMF = S0207974611
Jan 28 2008 15:45:21 -0500 noexist
Jan 28 2008 15:47:01 -0500 decode: DTMF = P17974611
Jan 28 2008 15:47:01 -0500 decode: The command contains a bad digit (S,P,A,B,C,D)
Jan 28 2008 15:47:53 -0500 decode: DTMF = 71
Jan 28 2008 15:47:53 -0500 decode: Invalid command length: 71

show what your node is doing, and include buttons or clickable links that let you send commands to it from a Web browser. When it's configured the right way, you can access it over the Internet from a Web browser anywhere in the world, giving you keyboard-and-mouse access to the main functions of your node.

Just as with the IVR approach, there are lots of different ways to make this happen. The *EchoLink* software has a built-in Web server that you can enable by checking a box on the Remt tab of the Sysop Settings page. It produces a useful but rather bare-bones Web page that shows recent activity in the log, and lets you enable or disable the node, or connect or disconnect from other nodes. You can even run the Web remote control and the dial-in remote control at the same time if you want the most flexibility when traveling about.

For *IRLP*, a simple way to set up Web remote control is to install the open-source Apache Web server, and then download and install a special Remote Admin (RA) package from the *IRLP* FTP site. This is a script written in the *PHP* programming language, which is installed on the Apache server. Like the *EchoLink* page, it gives you access to the most important node control functions without any bells and whistles (**Figure 10.4**). But if you are a *PHP* whiz, or if you're comfortable writing Web applications in some other language (or would like to learn), you can easily soup it up — the sky's the limit here!

If you carry around one of those fancy wireless PDAs or smart phones, an interesting twist on the Web remote control idea would be to create a set of Web pages that are ideally suited for the small screen of your PDA, or even a Wireless Application Protocol (WAP) interface. This would let you interact remotely with your node from the comfort of your own pocket.

Figure 10.4 — A screen shot of the *IRLP* Remote Admin (RA) page, running in the *Apache* Web Server on an *IRLP* node.

## Chapter 11

Legal Issues in Linking

There's been a great deal of confusion about the legal aspects of Internet linking. Part of the problem is that very few countries have recognized the concept of Internet linking in their Amateur Radio regulations. In the United States, for example, the Federal Communications Commission (FCC) rules governing the Amateur Radio Service make no mention of interconnecting radio transmitters to the Internet. This leaves hams in the position of having to interpret the more general rules relating to station control and third-party traffic.

In certain countries, however, the rules are a bit clearer. In the United Kingdom, for example, the Office of Communications (Ofcom) specifically allows amateurs to operate so-called "voice gateways" if they have obtained a special permit called a Notice of Variation (NoV). This NoV is an endorsement to an Amateur license that gives the licensee permission to operate a VoIP link on a specific frequency in the VHF or UHF bands.

Questions about this topic come up frequently, and the most important thing to remember is this: *Internet linking is legal if links are operated in a legal manner*, according to the rules. It's important to know the rules that might apply to VoIP Internet links in the country in which you live, and to be sure that your station is being operated according to those rules.

A DISCLAIMER

Before diving into this topic, let me first say that I am not an authority on Amateur Radio regulations around the world, nor am I an attorney. As a licensed Amateur Radio operator, it's your responsibility to read, understand, interpret, and comply with the rules that apply to your station, just as I have done. As a starting point, you might be interested in one ham's journey through his country's regulations. So what follows is *my own view* of how the regulations governing my station should be applied.

STATIONS AND SYSTEMS

One important point should be made right off the bat. Government agencies such as the FCC regulate Amateur *stations*, not *systems*. For example, it would not be accurate to use a phrase such as "the FCC rules about *EchoLink*." The FCC does not regulate *EchoLink*, *IRLP*, *eQSO*, nor any other computer system or software used with Amateur Radio. It does, however, regulate U.S. Amateur Radio stations. So what we're discussing here is how to legally operate a *station* that happens to have this type of system connected to it.

FCC RULES, PART 97

In the United States, Federal Communications Commission rules do not prohibit interconnection of Amateur stations with the Internet. However, the lack of any special regulations for this type of connection would seem to imply that all ordinary operating rules apply to the link station. For example, the link station would need to identify itself every ten minutes, stay within the limits on emission type, power and frequency, and have a designated control operator, just as if the station were not connected to the Internet. In other words, the act of connecting the station by voice to the Internet conveys no special operating rules or privileges.

The first stop is **Section 97.3, Definitions**. Here are some definitions of particular interest:

6) Automatic control. The use of devices and procedures for control of a station when it is transmitting so that compliance with the FCC rules is achieved without the control operator being present at a control point.

(7) Auxiliary station. An Amateur station, other than in a message forwarding system, that is transmitting communications point-to-point within a system of cooperating Amateur stations.

(12) Control operator. An Amateur operator designated by the licensee of a station to be responsible for the transmissions from that station to assure compliance with the FCC rules.

(13) Control point. The location at which the control operator function is performed.

(30) Local control. The use of a control operator who directly manipulates the operating adjustments in the station to achieve compliance with the FCC rules.

(31) Message forwarding system. A group of Amateur stations participating in a voluntary, cooperative, interactive arrangement where communications are sent from the control operator of an originating station to the control operator of one or more destination stations by one or more forwarding stations.

(38) Remote control. The use of a control operator who indirectly manipulates the operating adjustments in the station through a control link to achieve compliance with the FCC rules.

(39) Repeater. An Amateur station that simultaneously retransmits the transmission of another Amateur station on a different channel or channels.

(46) Third-party communications. A message from the control operator (first party) of an Amateur station to another Amateur station control operator (second party) on behalf of another person (third party).

INTERNET LINKS: A SPECIAL ANIMAL?

First, what type of station, in the eyes of the FCC, is a VoIP link? Is it a repeater, a message forwarding system, an auxiliary station, or none of the above?

Some have argued that a VoIP link counts as a repeater (as long as it's connected to an RF node at the other end), since its sole purpose in life is to retransmit the signals of another Amateur station. (One "benefit", incidentally, of defining it as a repeater is that it would qualify for automatic control.)

However, I see some problems with this. Certainly, when viewing the whole picture end-to-end, it is indeed true that the voice of mobile station A is being re-transmitted on a different channel to mobile station B, through the cooperation of link X and link Y. However, does that mean that Link Y — just one piece of the whole system — is considered a repeater in its own right? Keep in mind that Link X and Link Y are probably being operated under different call signs by different licensees, and might even be in different countries. Unlike a repeater system with remote receivers joined by telephone lines, in which the entire system is operated by one licensee as a single, cohesive system, Link X and Link Y have no regulatory relationship with each other, and (in my view) are not repeaters in their own right.

Others have claimed that a VoIP link counts as an auxiliary station, since it is "transmitting communications point-to-point within a system of cooperating Amateur stations". Maybe we're getting warmer. Systems like *IRLP* and *EchoLink* might each qualify as a system of cooperating Amateur stations, and the VoIP link, if it's tuned to the input frequency of a repeater, is certainly participating in point-to-point RF communications. And, most likely, the link licensee has set up his link in cooperation with the repeater licensee, further supporting the "cooperating stations" idea.

But what if the VoIP link is tuned to a simplex frequency rather than a repeater input — can this still be considered point-to-point communication? And would *every* station that fits this broad definition be considered an auxiliary station? If you sit down at your HF rig every night at 8 PM for a sked with a ham in Australia, you are certainly working point-to-point, and the two of you could be regarded as working in cooperation with each other. Does that make your station an auxiliary station, under the FCC's definition? If so, this practice would be illegal, since it occurs below 144 MHz!

This is an extreme example, to be sure, but the point is that the FCC's definition of "auxiliary station" is not very precise. It is often understood to apply to special, permanently-installed stations that are used to link repeaters (or components of repeaters, such as remote receivers) together, or for RF control links.

However, some Amateurs believe the auxiliary-station definition also applies to any station transmitting on the input frequency of a repeater, even if not part of the repeater system per se, and even if operated by a different licensee. Others believe that any Internet voice gateway, whether tuned to a repeater input or not, must be considered an auxiliary station, simply because it doesn't fit neatly into other categories. From the licensee's perspective, the "advantage" of such a view is that it would allow links to be automatically controlled, and the "disadvantage" is that it would prohibit them from operating below 144 MHz entirely.

But the purpose and spirit of the auxiliary-station definition, in my view, is to allow components of a repeater system (such as remote inputs) to communicate with each other under automatic control, and to ensure that they do not take up valuable spectrum below 144 MHz. The automatic-control provision for these auxiliary stations is what makes them practical.

In contrast, an Internet link tuned to the frequency pair of a local repeater uses no additional spectrum at all, regardless of the frequency band. When properly designed, its effect on the spectrum is the same as if it were being operated as a base station by an active ham — possibly even less. As such, it is the licensee's responsibility to ensure that it uses minimal power and doesn't cause harmful interference. Also, I see nothing in §97.3(a)(7) that suggests that the definition would apply to nodes operating on a simplex frequency, communicating with portable and mobile stations in the area.

Fortunately, Part 97 has a general provision for remotely controlled stations. Stated broadly, any US Amateur station may be operated under *remote control* with the same privileges as it may be operated under local control, and under the same set of rules — namely, that a control operator must be monitoring and in control of the station. Remote control can be done either using an auxiliary station, which must be above 144 MHz, or over a wireline link. Part 97 says a control link "using a fiber optic cable or another telecommunication service is considered wireline," so sending commands over a telephone line or over an Internet connection certainly seems to suffice. Under this provision, it seems that a VoIP link could be operated on any frequency available to both the control operator and the station licensee, as long as the control operator was always on duty, and had one of these methods of controlling the station remotely.

A question is often asked about the practice of sending DTMF commands over the input frequency of a 6-meter node. Wouldn't this be considered a control function, and therefore illegal below 144 MHz?

For one thing, I think there is a distinction here between a control *function* and a control *requirement*. For remotely-controlled stations, the FCC requires that a control link exist between the control point and the station, "sufficient for the control operator to perform his/her duties." The definition of remote control in §97.3 refers to making station adjustments over this link to achieve compliance with the rules. And §97.109(c) says simply "when a station is being remotely controlled, the control operator must be at the control point."

I interpret this to mean that the purpose of the control link is to help prevent the station from operating illegally — for example, to shut it down if it begins drifting off frequency, or if a QSO of a commercial nature takes place — and to have a sure-fire mechanism in place to do so. This doesn't necessarily mean that *all* control functions must be executed over this link, nor that every station that sends control signals is performing the duty of the control operator. In summary, the rules are clear about what constitutes a legal control link, and in which situations it is required, but do not appear to restrict the methods of station control beyond the basic requirement.

Secondly, the control functions commonly available to mobile and portable users through their DTMF keypad are usually not station control functions, strictly speaking. For the most part, these are signals for establishing and dropping Internet connections, rather than signals for switching a transmitter on and off or changing its frequency and power. What is being controlled is not the station (i.e., the transmitter), but the Internet connection behind it.

CONTROL OPERATORS AND THIRD PARTIES

So far so good — the VoIP link is under remote control. What then, is the role of the person that's communicating through it over the Internet? Is that person a control operator, a third party, or neither?

Some VoIP enthusiasts argue that the remote person is indeed a control operator, performing his or her duties remotely over the Internet. The trouble with this viewpoint is that the remote person doesn't have much control over the link, beyond disconnecting himself from it, or making it transmit. He might not even know what frequency it is operating on, nor at what power level, nor have any way of monitoring it to verify that it's working right. What's more, he might not even be qualified to be a control operator. Keep in mind that the remote station might be in a different country. FCC rules *do* specifically allow hams in other countries to be control operators of US stations, but only if a reciprocal operating agreement is in place.

Another possibility is that the remote person is considered a third party, similar to a non-ham speaking over a repeater through a phone patch. Since a control operator is present, it certainly seems legal under Part 97. Can a licensed ham be considered a third party? Nothing in the rules seems to disallow it. Do international third-party prohibitions apply? Not in my view. Section 97.115, which describes the third-party traffic restrictions, says "An Amateur station may transmit messages for a third party to…any station within the jurisdiction of the United States." If you are operating a VoIP link on a VHF or UHF frequency well within the borders of the US, this is almost certain to be the case! The rules do not place any restrictions on where the third party is located, only to where the RF transmissions are going. In this case, the long-haul, international path is indeed the public telecommunications system, rather than Amateur Radio.

Could the remote person be *neither* a control operator, *nor* a third party? I think in order for this to work, the remote person would have to be considered a *station*. This raises a couple of issues. It wouldn't apply if the remote person were sitting at a computer rather than a transmitter, since he wouldn't be emitting any RF of his own. And if the remote person is indeed operating a transmitter, as would be the case if he were working through a VoIP link at the other end, it's still complicated by the fact that his audio is being relayed over the Internet rather than being picked up by a receiver directly connected to the local VoIP link.

The upshot of all of this is that I would regard most VoIP links in the United States as ordinary Amateur stations, not repeater stations or auxiliary stations. This means that the link must be either locally or remotely controlled whenever it's on the air.

And that means there *must* be a control operator on duty when the link is transmitting, albeit someone listening at a distant control point.

If it's remotely controlled, the licensee (in the US) has the option of using either an RF control link or a wireline link for remote control. An RF control link must be an auxiliary station, and therefore in the 144-MHz band or above, and a wireline link can be either a conventional phone line or an Internet connection. Regardless of the type, there needs to be a 3-minute timer that shuts down the system automatically in case the control link goes dead. (A common implementation of this rule is to have a timer that limits any single transmission to 3 minutes.)

I also acknowledge that *some* VoIP links might qualify as auxiliary stations in their own right. But I think that in order to qualify, they would need to be part of a connection involving two or more repeaters within a "system of cooperating Amateur stations"; in order to be legal, they would have to be operating above 144 MHz; and in order to be automatically controlled, they could not carry third-party traffic.

STATION IDENTIFICATION

A frequently-asked question about VoIP nodes concerns station identification. How, and when, should a node identify itself?

First, let's look at the link station itself. Again, I'll focus on the FCC rules as an example. The answer certainly seems to be that a VoIP node should identify itself just like any other Amateur station — with its own station call sign, "at the end of each communication, and at least every ten minutes during a communication." It makes no difference whether the link is tuned to a simplex frequency or the input frequency of a repeater. Assuming you take the position that the link is neither an auxiliary station nor a repeater, the ID should simply be the station's call sign, with no special suffix. And note that there is no requirement that the station's call sign be the same as that of the repeater to which it is tuned — these are two separate stations in the eyes of the FCC. Finally, note that the call sign of the control operator makes no difference; the ID should be the call sign of the link station itself.

Now, let's consider the VoIP user at the other end, who is working through the link over the Internet. Nothing about the nature of the VoIP connection affects the ID rules. If the remote user were working through a local repeater or simplex frequency, he would identify his station in the usual fashion, by announcing his call sign. If he's sitting in front of a computer microphone, no station ID rules apply, since he's not operating an Amateur Radio station. (However, it's become common practice to use one's own call sign periodically in that situation, just as when operating on the air, to help keep track of who is speaking to whom.)

FCC rules allow a radiotelephone station to identify itself either by phone (which includes modulated Morse) or CW. Although a voice ID is usually faster than Morse, the advantage of a Morse ID is that it can be sent simultaneously with speech, so that it takes no additional transmission time.

THE FUTURE

Regulations do change as technology evolves. Witness the FCC rule changes to accommodate ASCII in the early 1980s, and digital message forwarding systems soon thereafter. Internet linking has already earned its stripes as an innovation that benefits the Amateur Radio Service, so perhaps it now deserves special consideration in Part 97.

## Chapter 12

Is This *Really* Ham Radio?

Next to the code/no-code debate, the legitimacy of Internet linking has been one of the most hotly-debated topics in Amateur Radio recently — and perhaps with good reason. Interconnecting Amateur Radio with the Internet isn't something that should be taken lightly, nor is it just a minor ripple in the pond of ham radio developments. In some ways, it's a fundamental shift in the way Amateur Radio is perceived.

The obvious problem is that the Internet is not radio. With a few exceptions, the web of the Internet is mostly strung of fiber and copper, with bridges, routers, switches, and modems in place of mixers, RF amplifiers, filters, and antennas. As RF experimenters we are apt to view the Internet as a competitor to radio. Certainly, it competes for our time. We feel this all too well as we sit in front of our e-mail programs and Web browsers when we could be spinning the dial in the ham shack instead. We also feel it when we hear our friends and neighbors talking about the wonders of Internet communication, yet returning a blank stare when we ask them if they know about what Amateur Radio can do. Only a few years ago, the response was likely to be, "Is that like CB?" Nowadays, even CB radio is unfamiliar to the public.

Of course, we know better. Having experienced it first-hand, we know that radio is the best way — sometimes, the *only* way — to get the message through in times of disaster. We know that traffic nets trump phone calls (and chat rooms) for efficiency every time. When the power goes out, most of our computers go down, but many of our radios stay up. Our radios aren't susceptible to viruses, worms, denial-of-service attacks, or becoming disconnected in the middle of a long, important message. And they work a lot better in the car, and in our hands, than most wireless Internet devices do.

"In today's world, at least, nothing is more efficient than the Internet, in terms of cost and speed, for moving a message from Point A to Point B"

But still, there are some marvelous things the Internet can do. The path from New York to Sydney isn't always good

> *"In July of 2003, WX4NHC, at the National Hurricane Center in Miami, received Claudette weather and damage reports from affected areas via both the HF Hurricane Watch Net and portable stations linked through the IRLP SKYWARN reflector"*

on 20-meter phone, but it's almost always perfect over e-mail. Compared to HF radio, the information rate is enormous — hundreds of megabits per second, potentially, rather than one kilobit. QRN isn't a problem, and the only QRM is the steady stream of junk e-mail. In today's world, at least, nothing is more efficient than the Internet, in terms of cost and speed, for moving a message from Point A to Point B, a great distance apart, with no loss of information.

I have pointed out to a few fellow hams that a time-traveling ham, who went to sleep in 1964 and woke up in 2004, might flip on the switch of an HF rig and declare that nothing had changed. Of course, this is an exaggeration — the proportion of AM, SSB, and CW signals has changed, and certainly the digital mode frequencies have a different flavor from the RTTY signals back then. But essentially, the activities of ragchewing, nets, and DXing are about the same as they were 40 years ago, and the modes most widely used on HF are still about the same. The equipment is a lot different (smaller, lighter, cooler, and probably better), but except for digital modes, the basic technology of communicating from one place to another is no more effective or efficient than it was in 1964.

Yet, during this time, communications technology has grown by leaps and bounds. The problem is that (arguably) the most dramatic innovations in recent years haven't been strictly about radio. Two interesting examples are wireless networking and cellular telephones. Both have been exploding in popularity in recent years in consumer markets. And guess what — both involve interconnecting RF devices with landlines, to achieve improved communications.

Why shouldn't Amateur Radio be part of this revolution? Hams, as always, have a great deal to contribute, and are absolute wizards at putting together pieces of a system to create something that's better than the sum of its parts.

In the first chapter of this book, I cited some recent examples of how the role of Amateur Radio in public service and emergency communications was greatly enhanced by its ability to harness the Internet. Even in the short history of Amateur Internet linking, there have been plenty of examples:

The disaster relief team working in North Carolina in the aftermath of Hurricane Isabel in the fall of 2003 made "extensive use" of *EchoLink* via a portable repeater. The 20-meter Salvation Army Team Emergency Network (SATERN) net then provided HF liaison for travel into the primary disaster area.

In July of 2003, WX4NHC, at the National Hurricane Center in Miami, received

Claudette weather and damage reports from affected areas via both the HF Hurricane Watch Net and portable stations linked through the *IRLP* SKWARN reflector.

Using a repeater in Louisiana linked to others across the state via *IRLP*, W4EHW was able to collect weather reports during 2003's Hurricane Lili from stations in the affected area that did not have HF radios.

A supertyphoon struck Guam in December of 2002. After several unsuccessful attempts to reach the island on HF, SATERN finally made contact via an *EchoLink* connection, and used it as a communications link between Guam and the SATERN national office in Chicago.

During the hurricane season of 2008, the ARRL Headquarters station (W1AW) used *EchoLink* to monitor emergency communications in the disaster areas during times when poor HF propagation made it difficult or impossible to receive these signals in New England.

The first section of Part 97 of the FCC rules is called "Basis and purpose." Even if you live outside of the FCC's jurisdiction, this section is an excellent outline of Amateur Radio's reason-for-being. It is quoted below. As you read through the items in §97.1, think about how Internet linking systems — the interconnection of Amateur Radio and the Internet — help to support these principles:

(a) Recognition and enhancement of the value of the Amateur service to the public as a voluntary noncommercial communication service, particularly with respect to providing emergency communications.

(b) Continuation and extension of the Amateur's proven ability to contribute to the advancement of the radio art.

(c) Encouragement and improvement of the Amateur service through rules which provide for advancing skills in both the communications and technical phases of the art.

(d) Expansion of the existing reservoir within the Amateur radio service of trained operators, technicians, and electronics experts.

(e) Continuation and extension of the Amateur's unique ability to enhance international goodwill.

Over the years, hams have gone from connecting telegraph keys to their radios, to connecting telephone receivers, television cameras, Teletype machines, personal computers, and GPS receivers. This has brought us radiotelegraphy, radiotelephony, ATV, RTTY, digital communications, and APRS, respectively, all of which advanced the state of the art and enhanced both the value of Amateur Radio to the public and its enjoyment by hams.

Let's add the Internet to that list and raise the bar even further. Should it be called "radiodigitalintertelephony"? That's kind of a mouthful. VoIP or Internet Linking seems to be the preferred term.

Whatever you want to call it, please take the ball and run with it. Set up an *IRLP*, *EchoLink*, *eQSO*, or *WIRES-II* gateway, and help Amateur Radio remain vibrant in the twenty-first century.

Web Resources

Here are some useful URLs for more information about Amateur Internet Linking.

IRLP
Internet Radio Linking Project
www.irlp.net

IRLP General Information Mailing List
www.irlp.net/mailman/listinfo/irlp

IRLP Owners' Discussion Group on Yahoo! (English)
groups.yahoo.com/group/irlp/

Speak Freely (Unix)
sourceforge.net/projects/speak-freely-u/

Speak Freely on Linux (implementation advice)
www.germane-software.com/SpeakFreely

EchoLink
EchoLink
www.echolink.org

***EchoLink* Software Documentation**
www.echolink.org/help

EchoLink Discussion Group on Yahoo! (English)
groups.yahoo.com/group/echolink

WIRES-II
WIRES-II (English)
www.vxstd.com/en/wiresinfo-en/

eQSO
eQSO
www.eqso.com

Asterisk and app_rpt
Asterisk
www.asterisk.org

Tiara Master Site
tiaratechnology.org

AllStar Link Network
allstarlink.org

DMK Engineering
dmkeng.com

iaxRPT (PC client)
www.xelatec.com/xipar/iaxrpt

Other Software
theBridge (conference server)
cqinet.sourceforge.net

EchoMac (EchoLink-compatible program for *Mac OS X*)
echomac.sourceforge.net

Glossary

ADPCM — Adaptive differential pulse code modulation. A waveform codec that records the difference between samples, rather than their actual values and adjusts the coding scale dynamically (or uses logarithmic coding).

access control — The process of granting or denying access to resources based on identity.

authentication — The process of identifying a person (or computer) to ensure they are who they claim to be. Successful authentication establishes identity.

buffer — A temporary storage area in a computer's memory. A buffer from which data is read in the same order as it was written is known as a first-in, first-out (FIFO) buffer.

cable modem — An RF modem designed to operate over cable TV lines, or a type of Internet service (provided by cable TV companies) that uses these devices.

codec — Compressor-decompressor (or coder-decoder). A computer program (or hardware device) that compresses or codes digitized audio or video into a more compact representation, and also decompresses or decodes it.

compression — The technique of transforming data into a format that takes up less storage space or less bandwidth. With *lossless* compression, the data retains the same amount of information; with *lossy* compression, the data is approximated.

conference server — A computer program that can interconnect multiple nodes in such a way that transmissions from one node are received by all others. Also called a "reflector" or "conference bridge."

conference — A group of nodes that are currently interconnected by a reflector, a conference server, or a node that supports conferencing. Each such node is said to be "in conference." Transmissions from any participant in the conference are sent to all others.

conferencing — A feature available on some nodes that allows multiple nodes to be joined together in a conference, in the same manner as a conference server. The node's own RF gateway is always a participant in such a conference.

CTCSS — Continuous tone-controlled squelch system. A squelch system that responds to the presence of a low-pitched audio tone, rather than the quieting of the FM receiver, to detect an incoming signal. Motorola's implementation of CTCSS is called PL.

DHCP — Dynamic host configuration protocol. A system for automatically assigning an IP address to a computer when it is first started.

digital certificate — A digitally-signed document that contains information about a person or organization, along with the person or organization's public key. It is usually signed by a trusted organization that has verified its authenticity.

digital signature — The digest (digital summary) of a message, encrypted with the sender's private key. With the corresponding public key, the recipient of a message can use the digital signature to verify that the contents of the message have not been altered, and to verify the authenticity of the sender.

DSL — Digital Subscriber Line. A technology that allows digital signals to be carried over twisted-pair telephone lines. Often used to provide Internet access.

DTMF — Dual tone multi-frequency. A signaling system in which digits and special characters are transmitted as pairs of tones over a voice channel. Also called Touch-Tone.

firewall — Computer equipment (or software) that blocks undesired network communication, usually to or from the Internet for security reasons.

flow — In a router, a temporary rule that allows packets of data to continue running from one computer to another once a connection between them has been established.

free software—software that can be installed, viewed and modified without restriction. Free software is available as source code that can usually be downloaded from an Internet site free of charge, and is therefore both "free, as in speech" (unrestricted) and "free as in beer" (available at no cost.)

forwarding — A feature available in most Network Address Translation (NAT) routers that allows all incoming packets addressed to a specific port to be routed to a specific computer.

GSM — 1) A type of digital cellular telephone system. 2) The audio codec developed for this system, which carries voice at 13 kbps.

interface — In the context of Internet linking, a circuit that joins a receiver and transmitter (or transceiver) to a node's computer equipment. The interface usually connects to the computer's serial or parallel port, the computer's sound card, and the microphone, speaker, PTT, and carrier-detect terminals of the transceiver.

IP — Internet protocol. The set of packet-oriented digital communications protocols used by hosts on the Internet and other networks.

IVR — Integrated voice response system. A system that provides information to a telephone caller automatically, or collects information from the caller, through a series of voice prompts.

jitter — Unpredictable variations in latency over time, usually due to network congestion.

latency — The time it takes for data to move from one point to another through a network, or to be transformed from one form to another.

link — A station that forms a voice gateway between Amateur Radio frequencies and the Internet. Also called an "RF node."

Linux — The kernel of an open-source, Unix-type operating system that runs on many different types of computers, from PCs to mainframes. Also refers to the entire operating system built around the *Linux* kernel. Some distributions of *Linux* are available free of charge.

NAT — Network address translation. A feature of some routers that allows several computers on a local network to share a single Internet address, by re-addressing incoming and outgoing packets.

net — A conference that is established at a designated time, often to discuss a specific topic.

node — In the context of Internet linking, a computer equipped with VoIP software that can communicate over the Internet with others so equipped. A node can be a station that forms a voice gateway between Amateur Radio frequencies and the Internet, a stand-alone computer that communicates with other nodes over the Internet, or a conference server. An RF node is also called a "link" or "voice gateway."

node number — A number that uniquely identifies a node. Node numbers are usually assigned by VoIP system administrators.

NoV — Notice of Variation. A license endorsement granted by the Office of Communication in the U.K. An NoV for Internet Voice Gateway operation is currently required for Amateurs who wish to operate an RF node in the U.K.

PBX — Private branch exchange. A device that acts as a telephone switch, routing calls between telephone lines and telephones. A PBX usually controls telephones and lines only at a single location or office.

PCM — Pulse code modulation. A digital representation of an audio signal in which each value is directly proportional to the amplitude of the corresponding sample.

peer — A node that is currently connected to one or more other nodes.

peer-to-peer — Communication that takes place directly from one node to another (over the Internet), rather than through a central server.

PGP — Pretty Good Privacy. A set of cryptographic functions that can be used for encrypting or digitally signing messages that are sent over the Internet.

POTS — Plain Old Telephone Service. A nickname for the set of standards that describe conventional, "twisted-pair" analog telephone service.

private key — In public-key cryptography, the key that is kept secret by the sender of a signed message, or by the recipient of an encrypted message. A message signed with the private key can be verified with the matching public key, and a message encrypted with the public key can only be decrypted with the matching private key.

public key — In public-key cryptography, the key that is disclosed by the sender of a signed message, or by the recipient of an encrypted message. A message encrypted with the public key can only be decrypted with the matching private key.

pulseback — A situation in which a node transmits to the Internet due to a false COS signal when the link transmitter goes key-up. The typical cure is to adjust the software's pulseback (or "anti-thump") timer so that it ignores the false COS signal.

reflector — 1) An *IRLP* conference server. 2) A computer program that receives e-mail messages and sends a copy of each to every subscriber in a list.

router — A device that connects to two or more networks and relays data from one to another. For example, a router may be installed between the Internet and a local-area network. Most routers can also act as simple firewalls.

script — A computer program, written in a scripting language, to be processed by a script interpreter or shell. Usually, a script is a series of commands that are interpreted and executed line-by-line, rather than being compiled into the native language of the computer.

scripting language — A computer programming language suitable for creating scripts.

trustee — The licensed Amateur responsible for operation of a node. Usually, but not always, the owner of the equipment and/or the licensee of the station.

validation — The process of initial authentication and license verification performed by VoIP system administrators when new users request access to the system.

VoIP — Voice-over-Internet protocol. The technique of using the Internet as a medium to carry voice signals by digitizing the voice, compressing it, and sending it as IP packets to a peer.

WAV — A file format, developed by Microsoft and IBM, for storing waveform audio data. A WAV file can contain data encoded in any of several different forms, such as PCM, ADPCM, and GSM.

Index

Notes

Notes

Notes

Please use this form to give us your comments on this book and what you'd like to see in future editions, or e-mail us at **pubsfdbk@arrl.org** (publications feedback). If you use e-mail, please include your name, call, e-mail address and the book title, edition and printing in the body of your message. Also indicate whether or not you are an ARRL member.

Where did you purchase this book?
☐ From ARRL directly   ☐ From an ARRL dealer

Is there a dealer who carries ARRL publications within:
☐ 5 miles   ☐ 15 miles   ☐ 30 miles   of your location?   ☐ Not sure.

License class:
☐ Novice   ☐ Technician   ☐ Technician Plus   ☐ General   ☐ Advanced   ☐ Extra

---

Name _____

Daytime Phone   (   ) _____

Address _____

City, State/Province, ZIP/Postal Code _____

If licensed, how long? _____

Other hobbies _____

_____

Occupation _____

ARRL member?   ☐ Yes ☐ No

Call Sign _____

Age _____

E-mail _____

For ARRL use only	INTERNET
Edition	2 3 4 5 6 7 8 9 10 11 12
Printing	1 2 3 4 5 6 7 8 9 10 11 12

From _____

_____

_____

EDITOR, INTERNET LINKING FOR RADIO AMATEURS
ARRL—THE NATIONAL ASSOCIATION FOR AMATEUR RADIO
225 MAIN STREET
NEWINGTON CT 06111-1494

— — — — — — — — — — please fold and tape — — — — — — — — — — — —